The other side of **OASIS**

CW00421370

Tablature & Instructions Explained

The tablature stave comprises six lines,

each representing a string on the guitar as illustrated

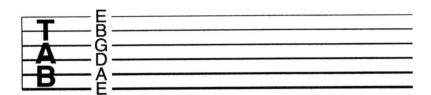

A number on any of the lines indicates, therefore,

the string and fret on which a note should be played

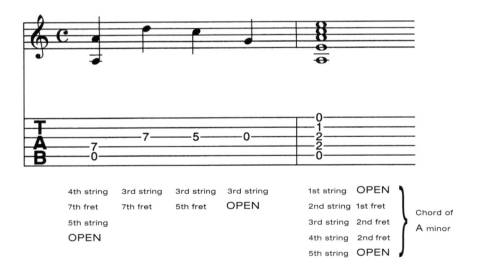

4th string	3rd string	3rd string	3rd string	1st string OPEN
7th fret	7th fret	5th fret	OPEN	2nd string 1st fret
5th string				3rd string 2nd fret
OPEN				4th string 2nd fret
				5th string OPEN

Chord of A minor

A useful hint to help you read tablature is to cut out

small squares of self-adhesive paper and stick them on the

upper edge of the guitar neck adjacent to each fret,

numbering them accordingly

Be careful to use paper that will not damage the finish on your guitar

Finger Vibrato

Tremolo Arm Vibrato

Glissando

Gliss

Strike the note, then slide

the finger up or down

the fretboard as indicated

Tremolo Strumming

This sign indicates

fast up and down

stroke strumming

8va

This sign indicates that

the notes are to be played an

octave higher than written

loco

This instruction

cancels the above

This note-head indicates

the string is to be totally muted

to produce a percussive effect

P.M. = Palm Mute

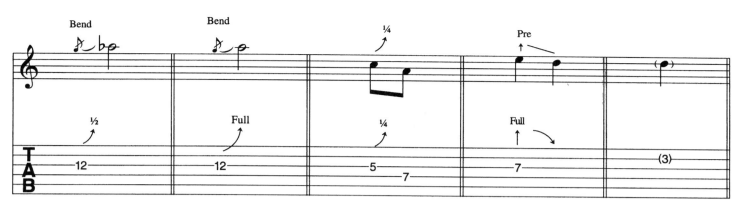

Half Tone Bend
Play the note G then
bend the strings so that
the pitch rises by
a half tone (semi-tone)

Full Tone Bend

Decorative Bend

Pre-Bend
Bend the string
as indicated, strike the
string and release

Ghost Note
The note is
half sounded

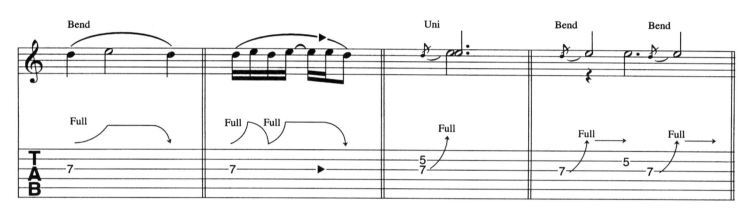

Bend & Release
Strike the string, bend it
as indicated then release
the bend whilst it is
still sounding

Bend & Restrike
Strike the string, bend or
gliss as indicated, then
restrike the string where
the symbol occurs

Unison Bend
Strike both strings
simultaneously then immediately
bend the lower string as
indicated

Staggered Unison Bend
Strike the lower string and
bend as indicated; whilst
it is still sounding strike the
higher string

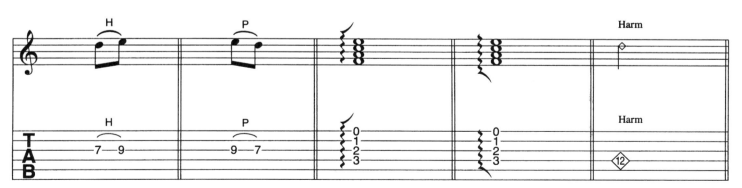

Hammer-On
Hammer a finger down
on the next note without
striking the string again

Pull-Off
Pull your finger off
the string with a plucking
motion to sound the next note
without striking
the string again

Rake-Up
Strum the notes
upwards in the manner
of an arpeggio

Rake-Down
Strum the notes
downwards in the manner
of an arpeggio

Harmonics
Strike the string whilst
touching it lightly at
the fret position shown

Artificial harmonics (A.H.), will
be described in context

Acquiesce

Words & Music by Noel Gallagher

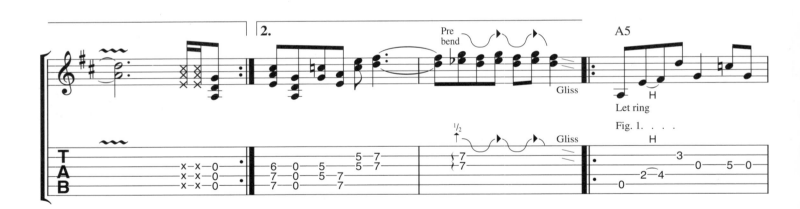

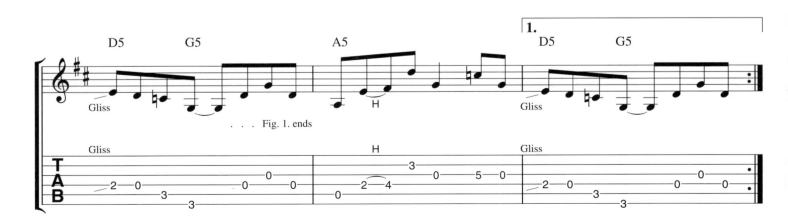

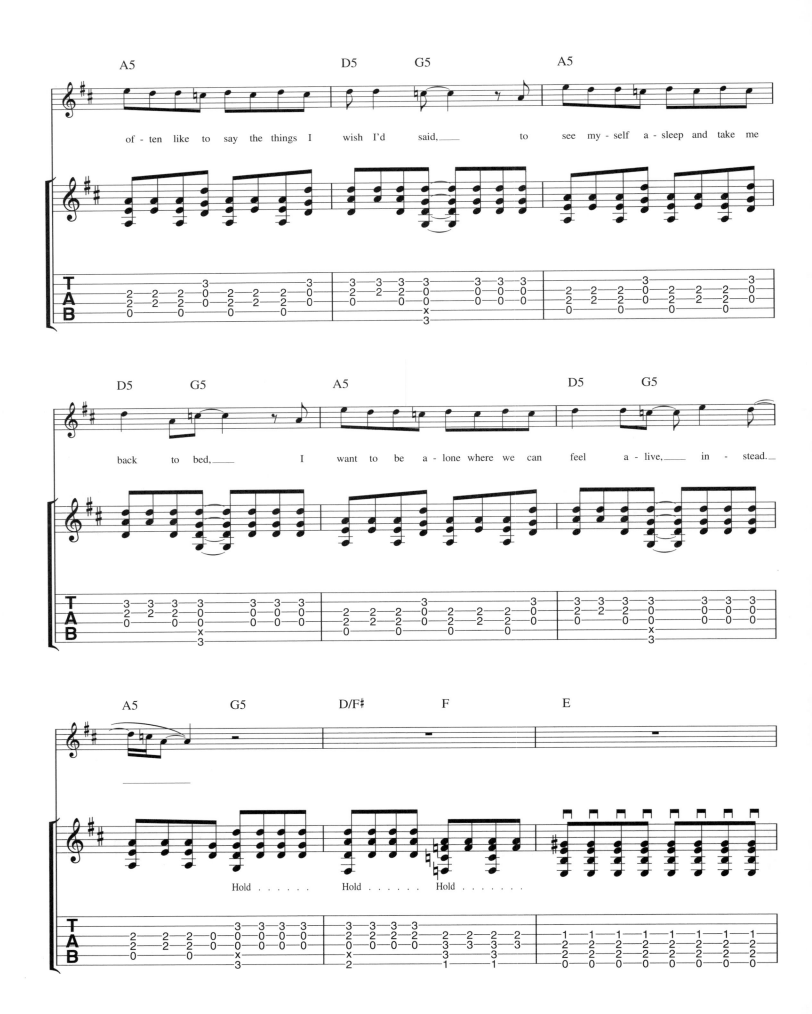

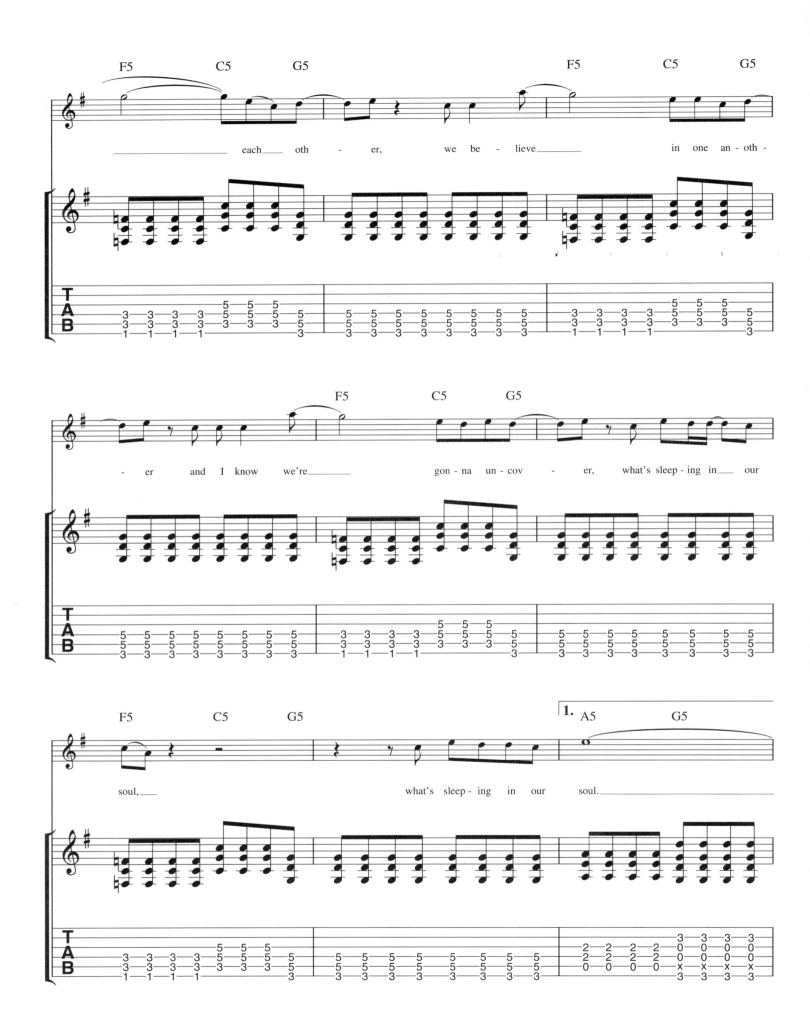

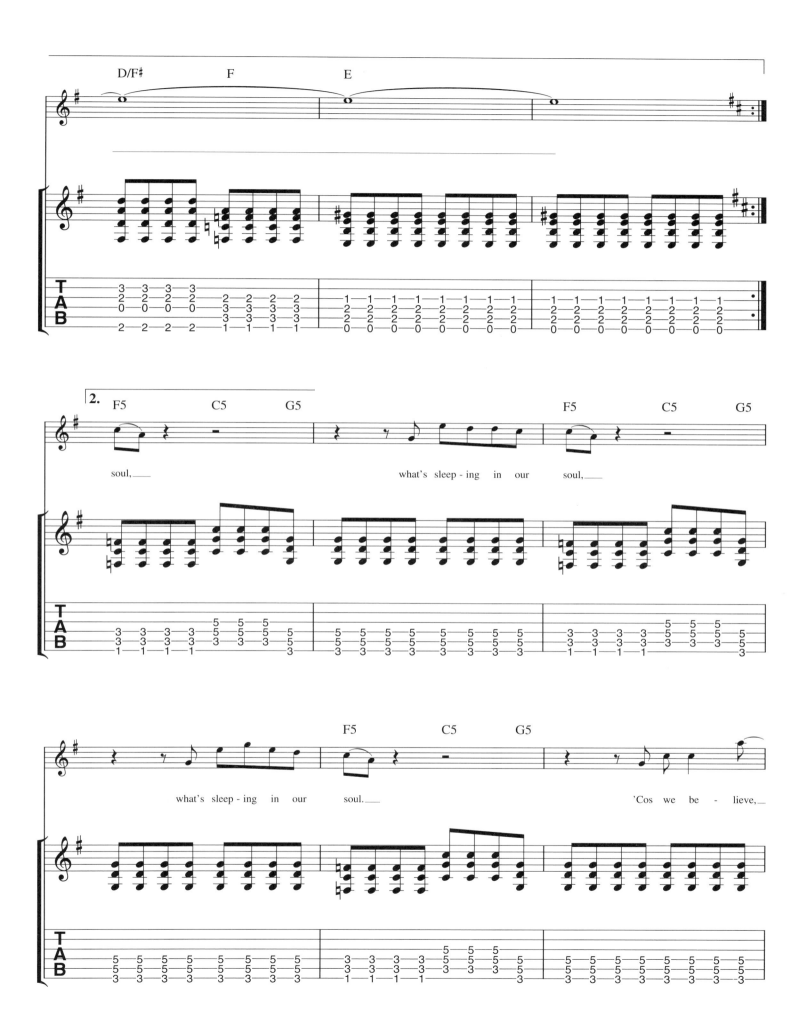

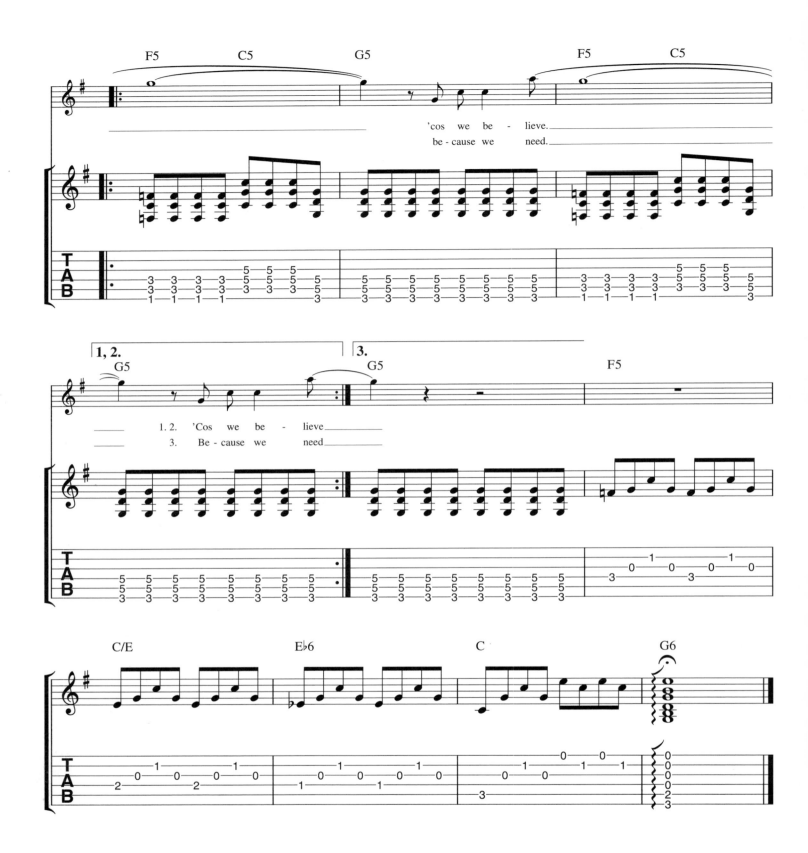

Verse 2:

There are many things that I would like to know
And there are many places that I wish to go
But everything's depending on the way the wind may blow.

I don't know what it is that makes me feel alive
I don't know how to wake the things that sleep inside
I only wanna see the light that shines behind your eyes.

D'Yer Wanna Be A Spaceman

Words & Music by Noel Gallagher

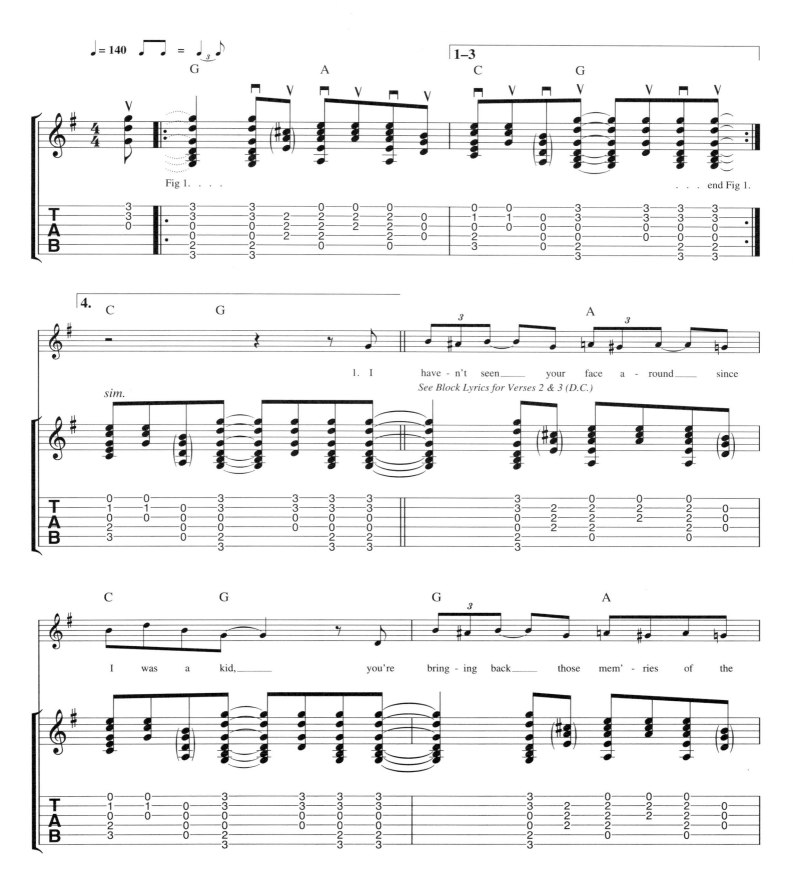

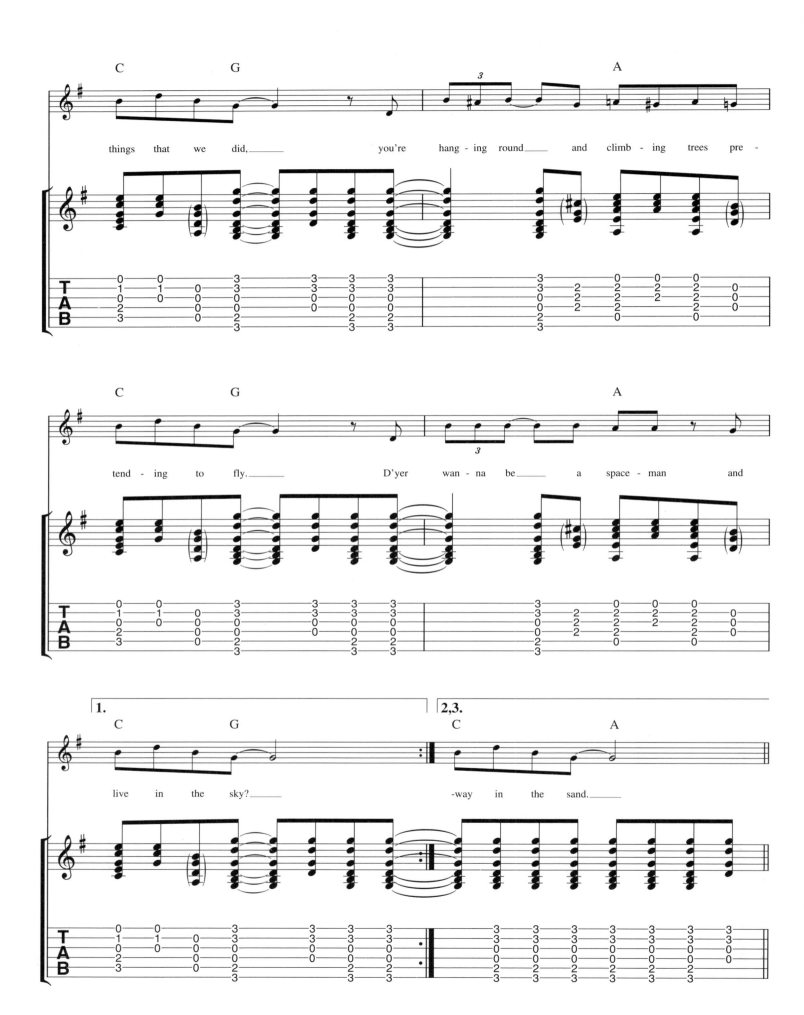

things that we did,_____ you're hang - ing round_____ and climb - ing trees pre -

tend - ing to fly._____ D'yer wan - na be_____ a space - man and

1.

live in the sky?_____

2,3.

-way in the sand._____

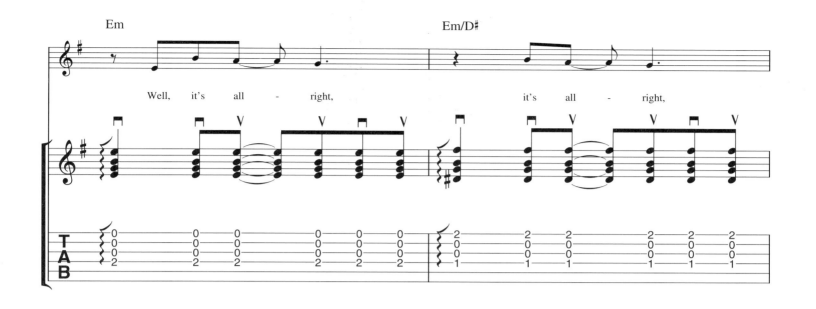

Well, it's all - right,   it's all - right,

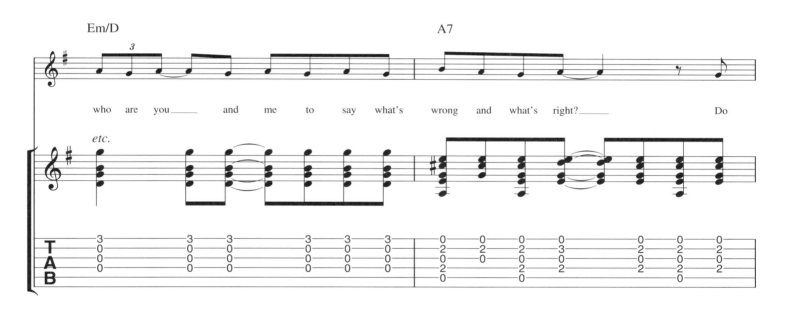

who are you____ and me to say what's wrong and what's right?____ Do

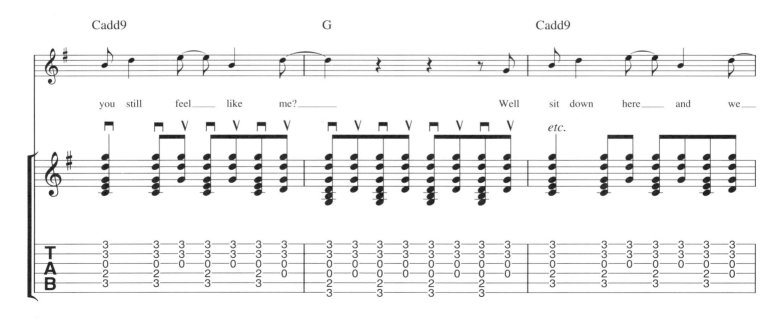

you still feel____ like me?____ Well sit down here____ and we____

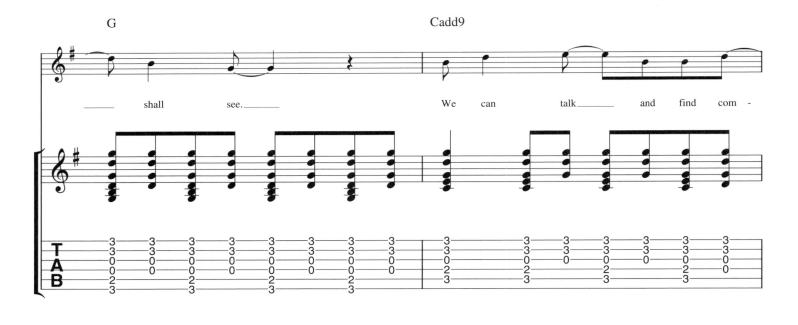

G   Cadd9

_____ shall   see._____   We   can   talk_____ and   find   com -

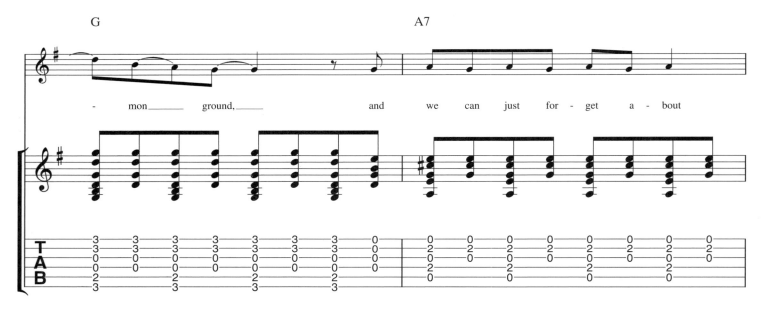

G   A7

- mon_____ ground,_____   and   we   can   just   for - get   a - bout

To Coda ✛
D.C. al ✛ *Coda*

G5/F   D/F♯

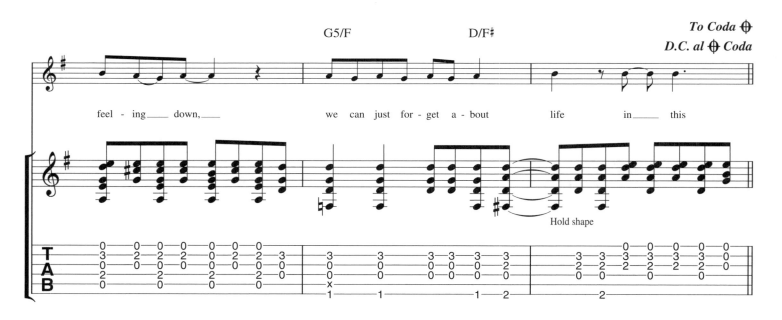

feel - ing_____ down,_____   we   can   just   for - get   a - bout   life   in_____ this

Hold shape

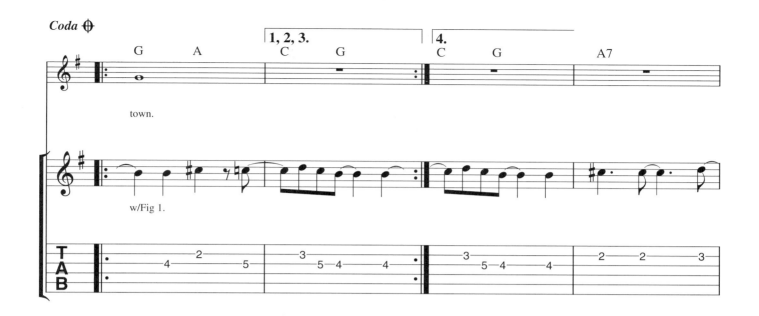

town.

w/Fig 1.

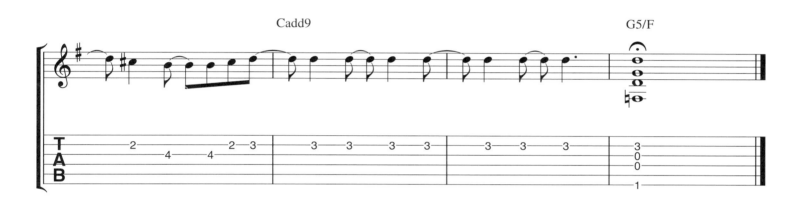

Verse 2:   You got how many bills to pay and how many kids?
               And you forgot about the things we did
               The town where we're living has made you a man
               And all of your dreams are washed away in the sand.

Verse 3 (D.C.) It's funny how your dreams change as you're growing old
               You don't wanna be no spaceman you just want the gold
               All the trained stealers are lying in wait
               But if you wanna be a spaceman it's still not too late.

Alive

Words & Music by Noel Gallagher

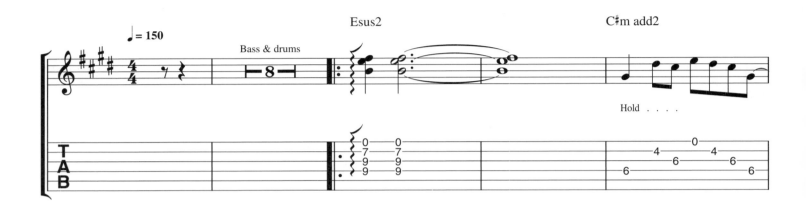

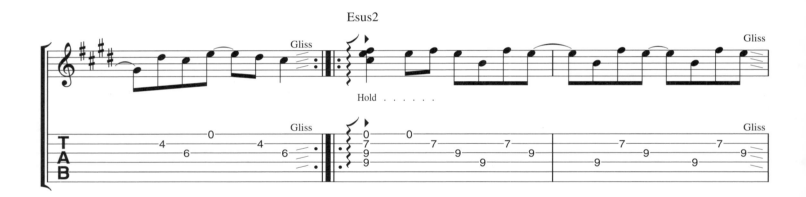

Verse:

1. The peo - ple will
See Block Lyrics for Verse 2.

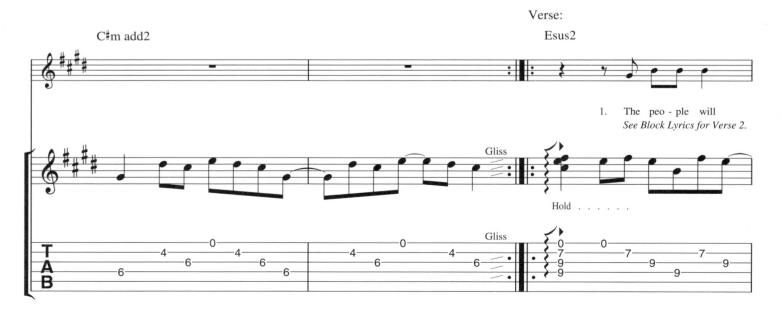

no - tice that the times   are change - in',_____

it's just for   now_____   but not____ for   good._____

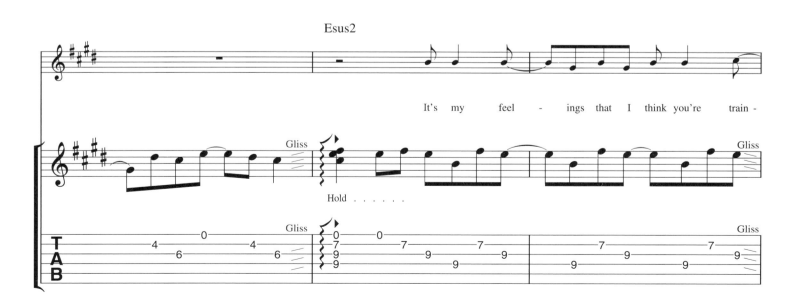

It's my   feel - ings that I think you're   train -

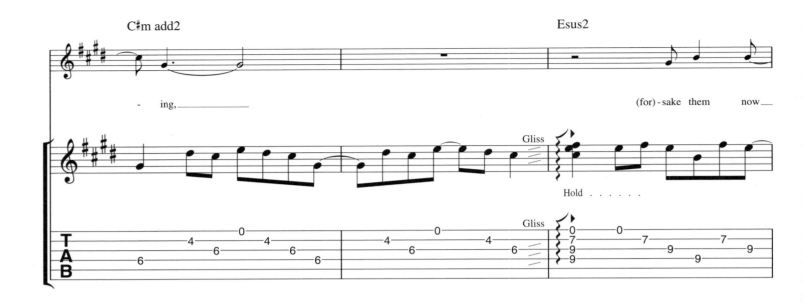

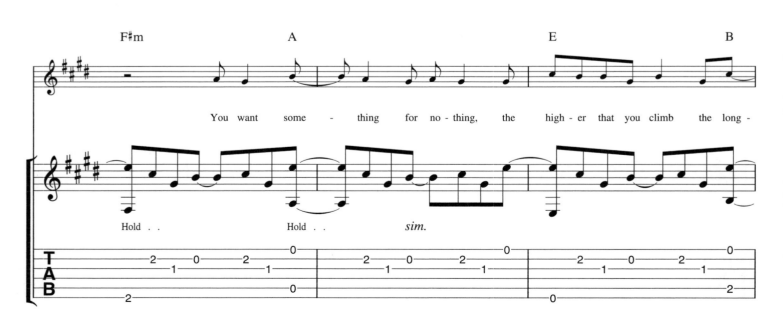

20

-er you fall.____ May - be your_____ time is com - ing,

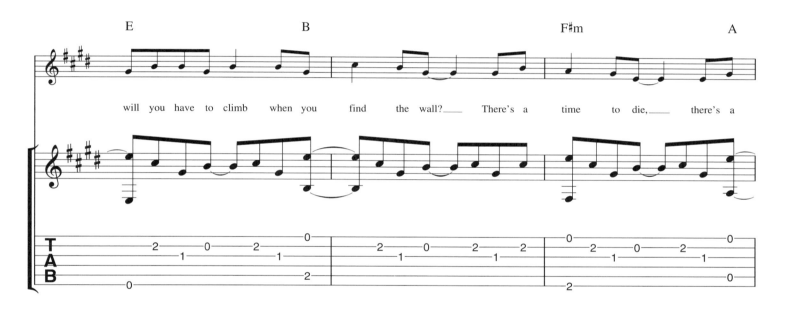

will you have to climb when you find the wall?____ There's a time to die,____ there's a

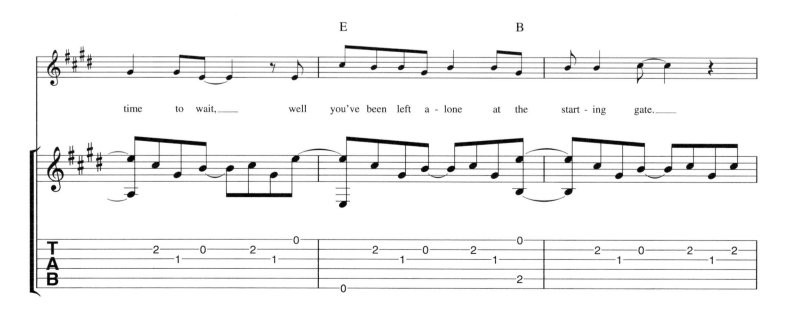

time to wait,____ well you've been left a - lone at the start - ing gate.____

F#m

I'm not blind____ and I____ don't mind____ 'cause I got time____ now I'm____

E   A   E

____ a - live.____   (Yeah,____ I'm a -

◻ = downstroke   V = upstroke

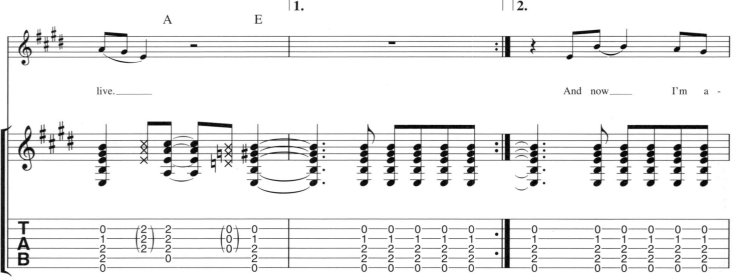

A   E   1.   2.

live.____   And now____ I'm a -

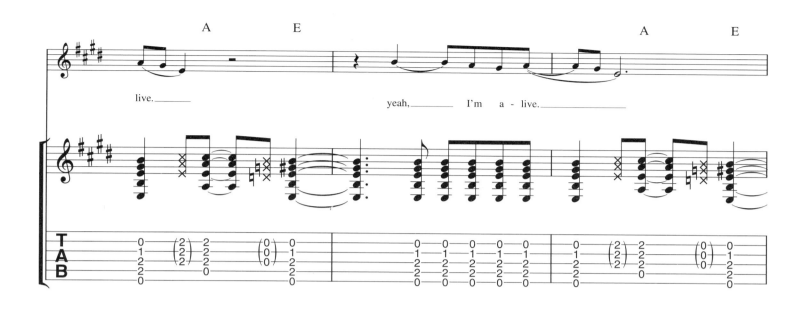

live._____

yeah,_____ I'm a - live._____

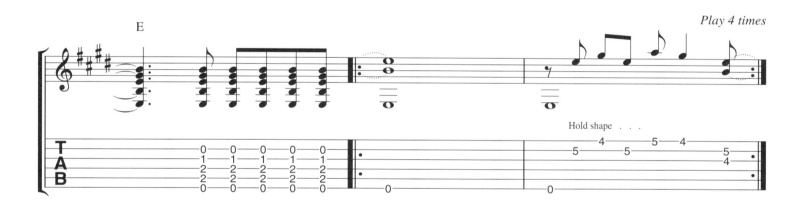

Play 4 times

Hold shape . . .

Play 3 times

Hold shape

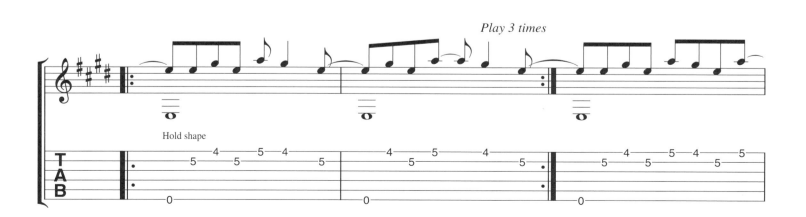

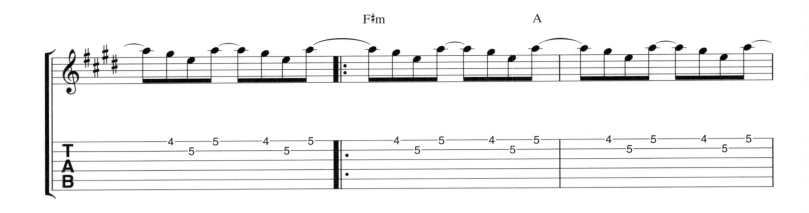

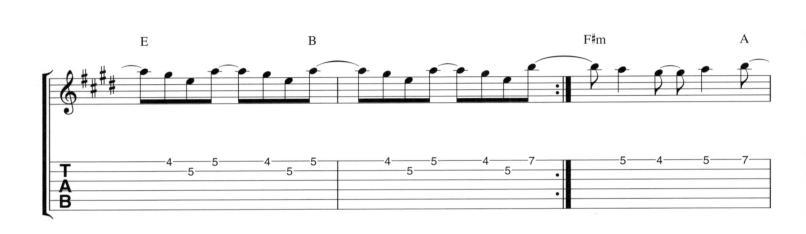

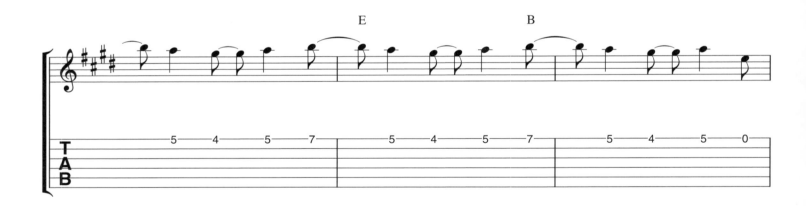

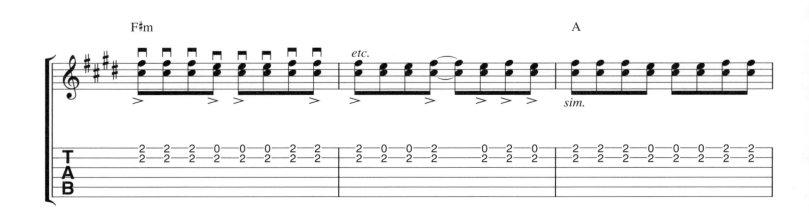

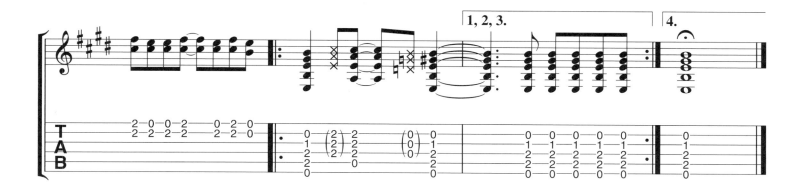

Verse 2:   The people have noticed that the times are changing
            But are they going to be something now
            I think I've seen you all hesitating
            I think I'll go and do something now.

Cloudburst

Words & Music by Noel Gallagher

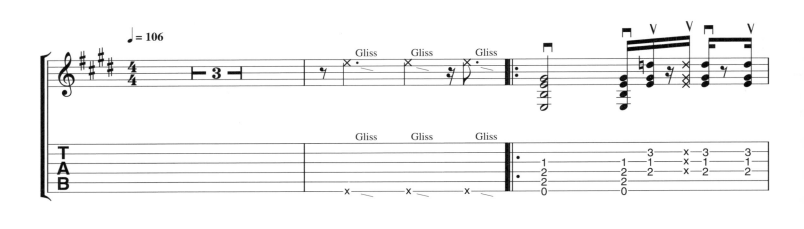

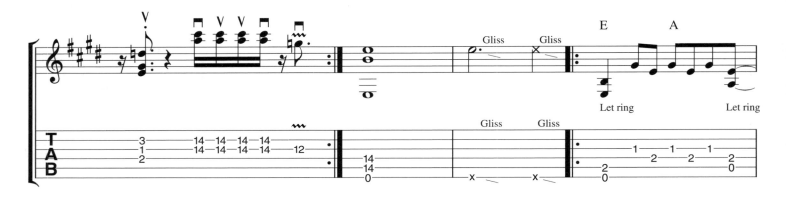

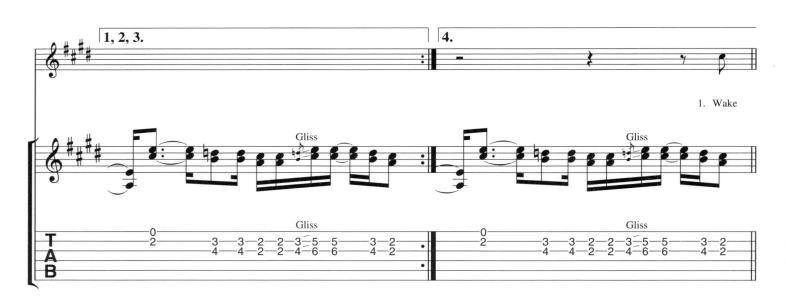

Verse:

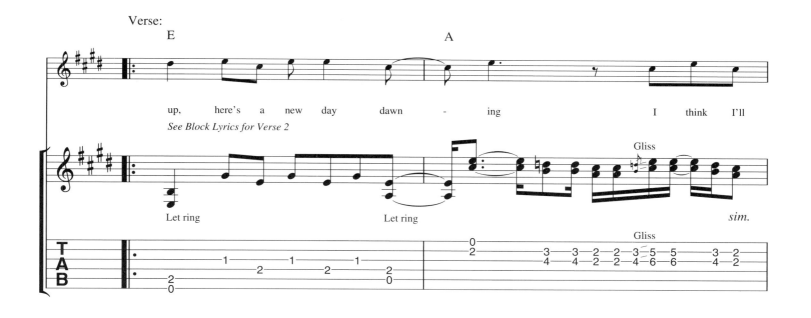

up, here's a new day dawn - ing   I think I'll

See Block Lyrics for Verse 2

Let ring   Let ring   *sim.*

take a lit - tle walk for a while.____   I need

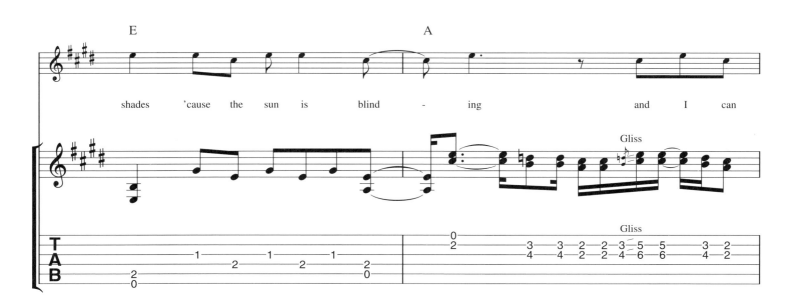

shades 'cause the sun is blind - ing   and I can

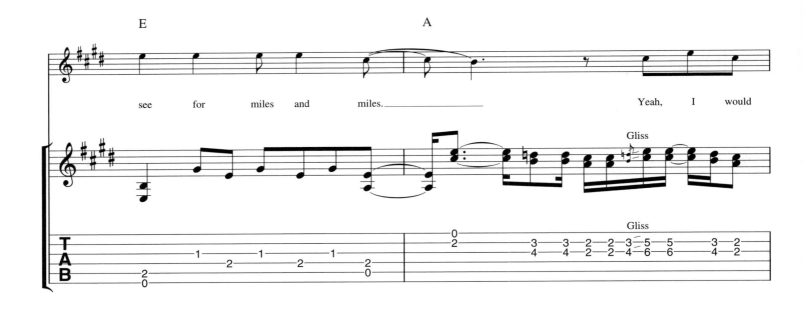

see   for   miles   and   miles._____   Yeah,   I   would

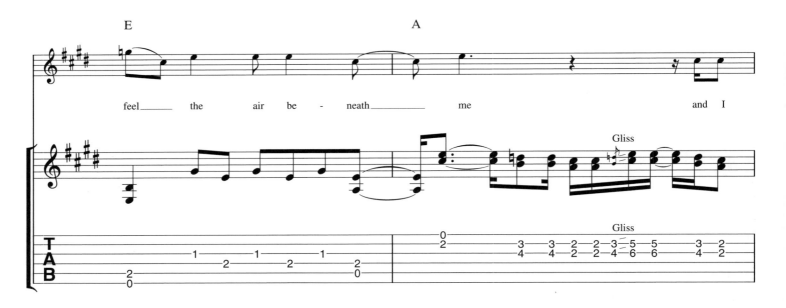

feel_____   the   air   be - neath_____   me   and   I

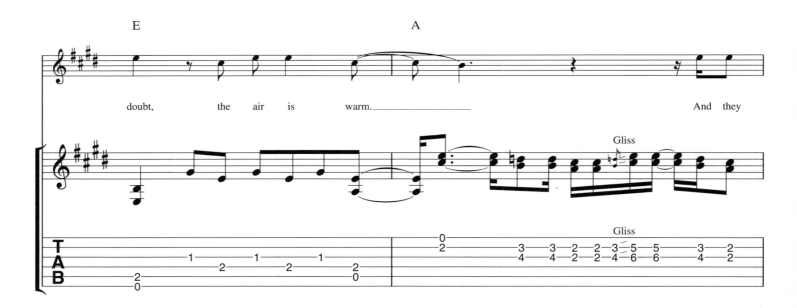

doubt,   the   air   is   warm._____   And   they

look but they can - not find_____ me, I'm

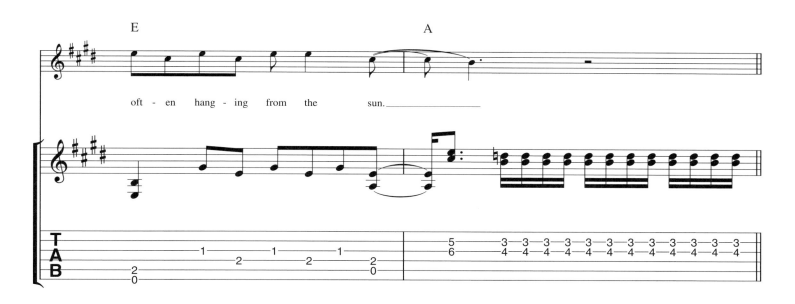

oft - en hang - ing from the sun._____

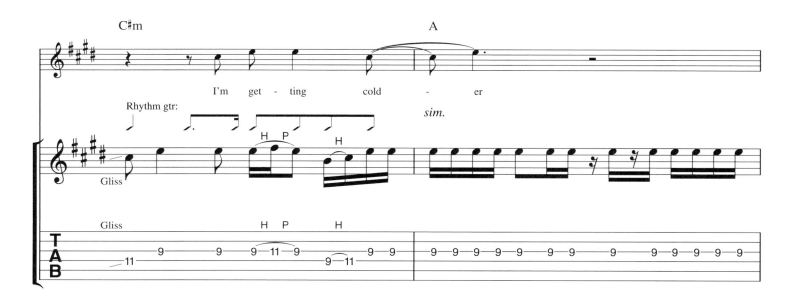

I'm get - ting cold - er

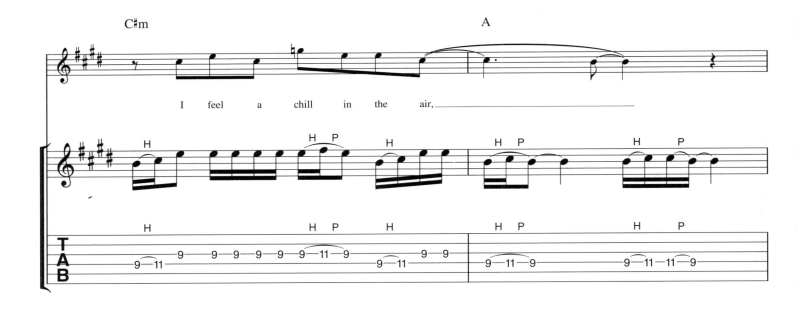

I feel a chill in the air,_____

There's a change in the wea - ther,

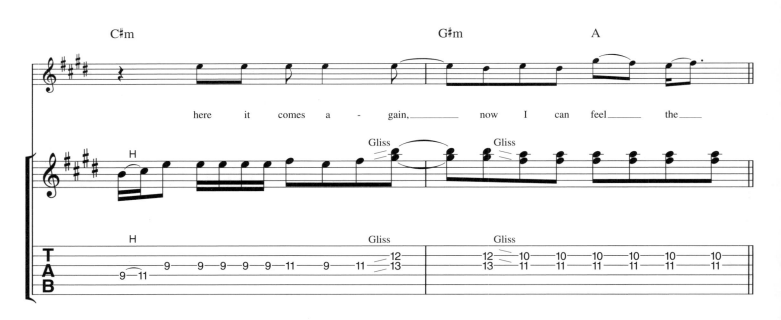

here it comes a - gain,_____ now I can feel_____ the_____

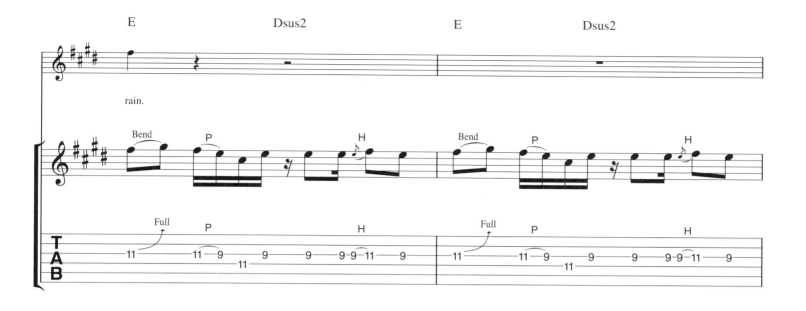

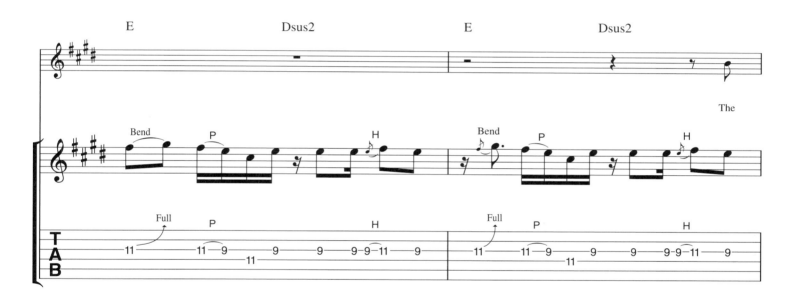

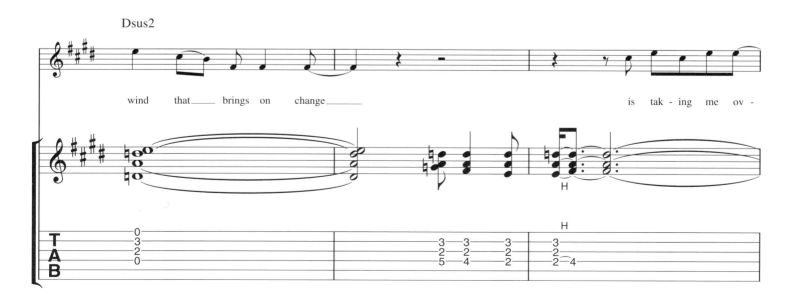

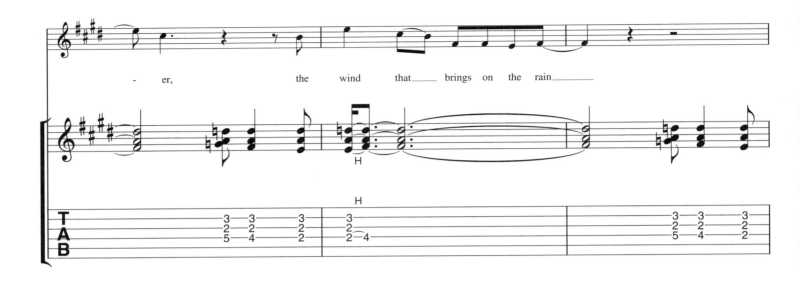

- er,   the wind that____ brings on the rain____

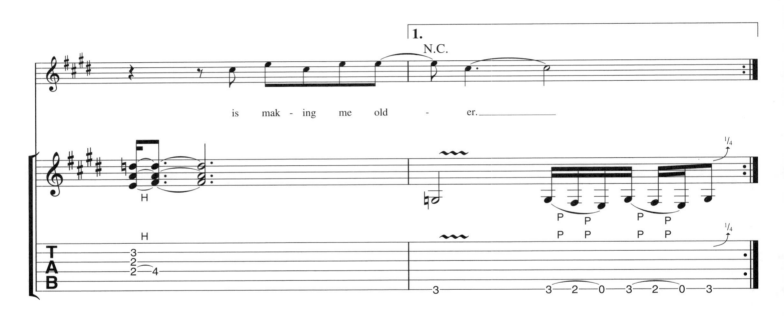

1.

is mak - ing me old - er.____

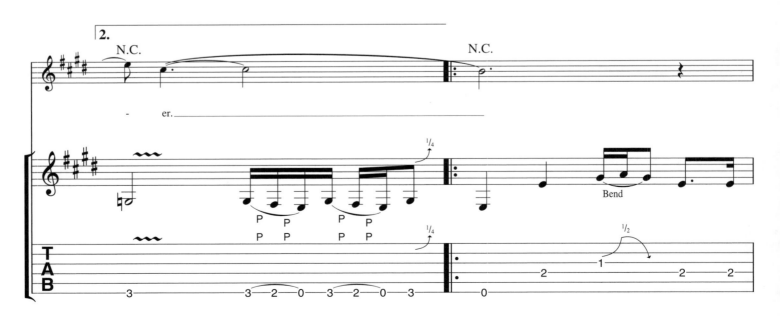

2.

- er.____

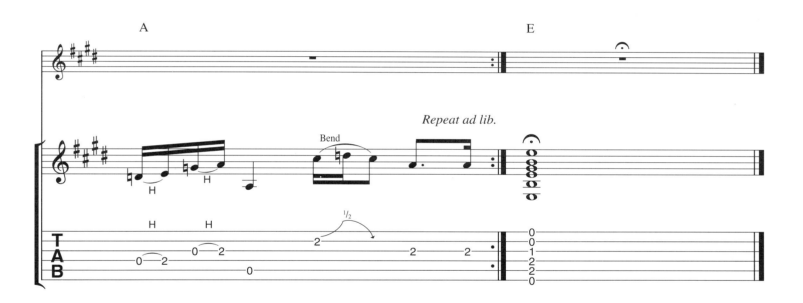

Verse 2:   *8 bars instrumental*
Down south the moon is shining
I'm gonna dress it up in style
My business everybody is minding
I need to get away for a while

33

Fade Away

Words & Music by Noel Gallagher

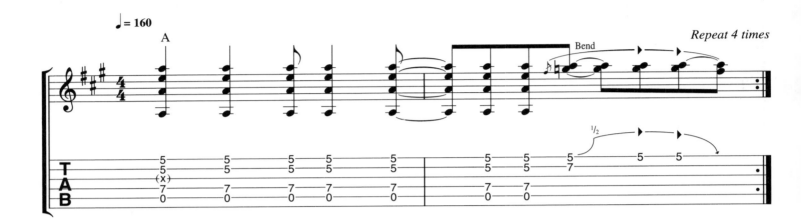

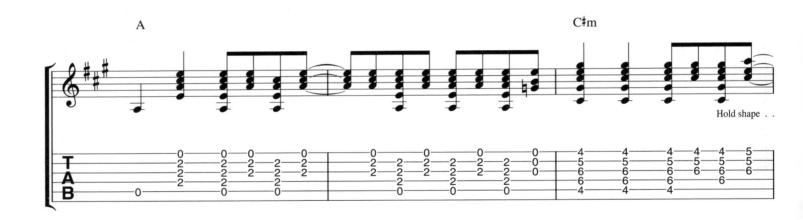

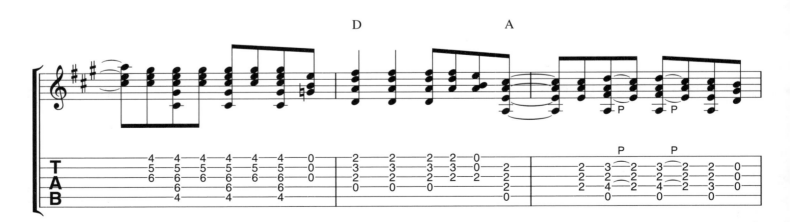

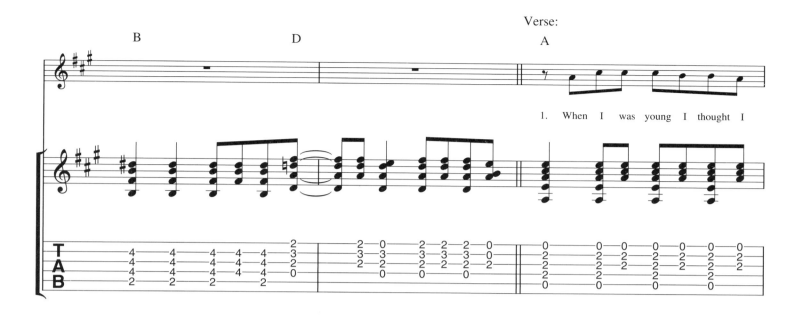

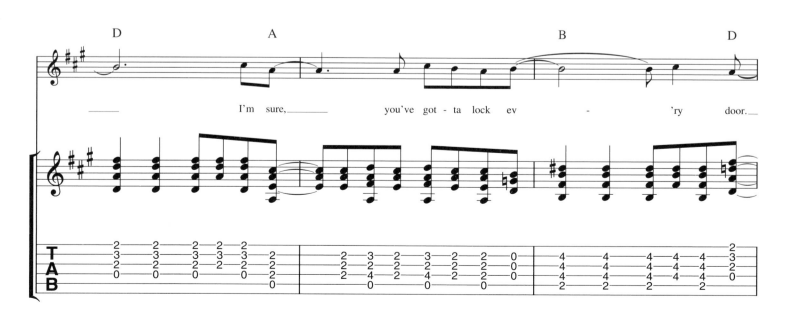

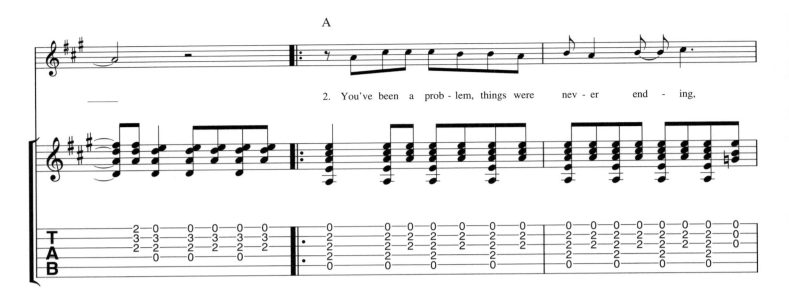

2. You've been a prob - lem, things were nev - er end - ing,

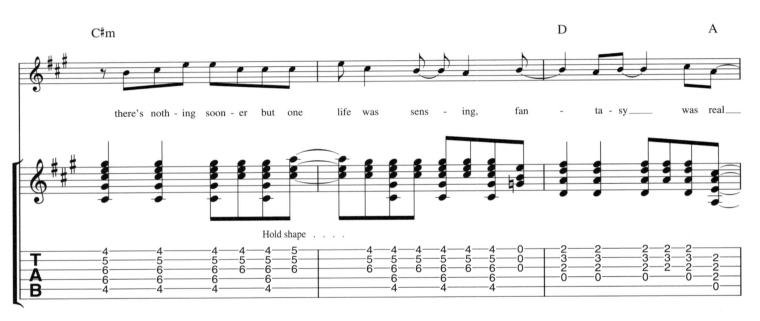

there's noth - ing soon - er but one life was sens - ing, fan - ta - sy____ was real____

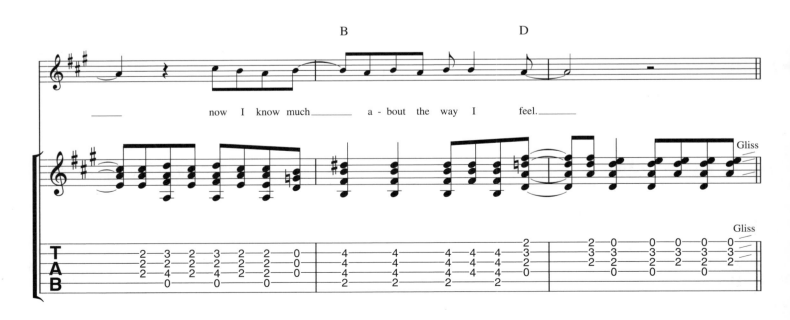

____ now I know much____ a - bout the way I feel.____

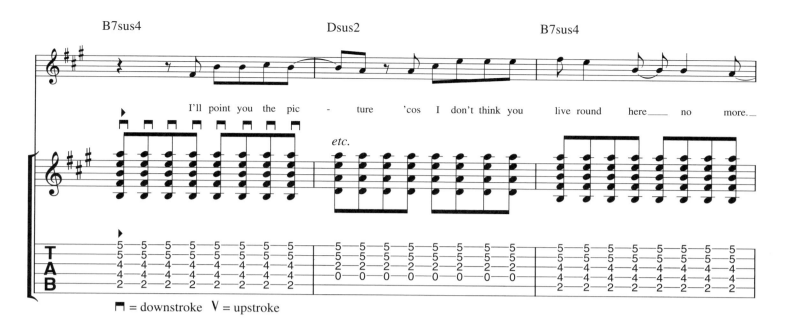

B7sus4　　　　　Dsus2　　　　　B7sus4

I'll point you the pic - ture 'cos I don't think you live round here___ no more.___

etc.

☐ = downstroke V = upstroke

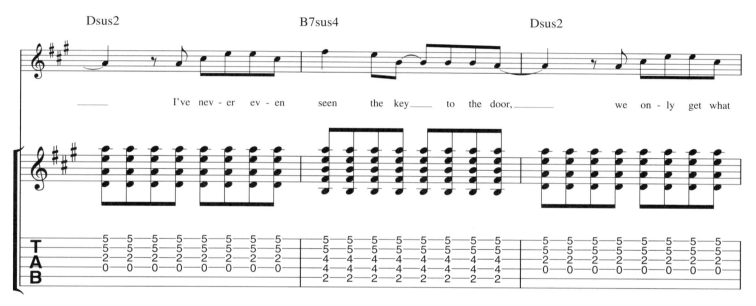

Dsus2　　　　　B7sus4　　　　　Dsus2

___ I've nev - er ev - en seen the key___ to the door,___ we on - ly get what

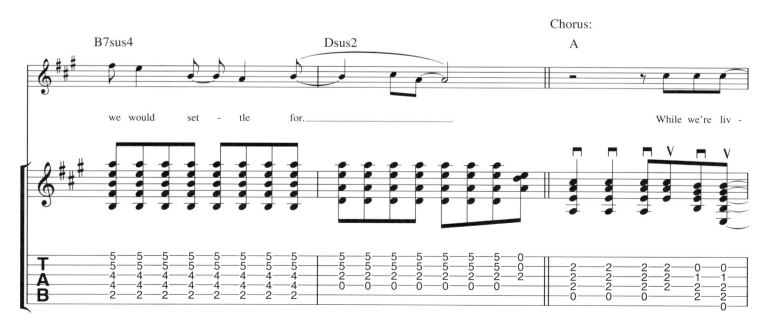

Chorus:

B7sus4　　　　　Dsus2　　　　　A

we would set - tle for.___ While we're liv -

37

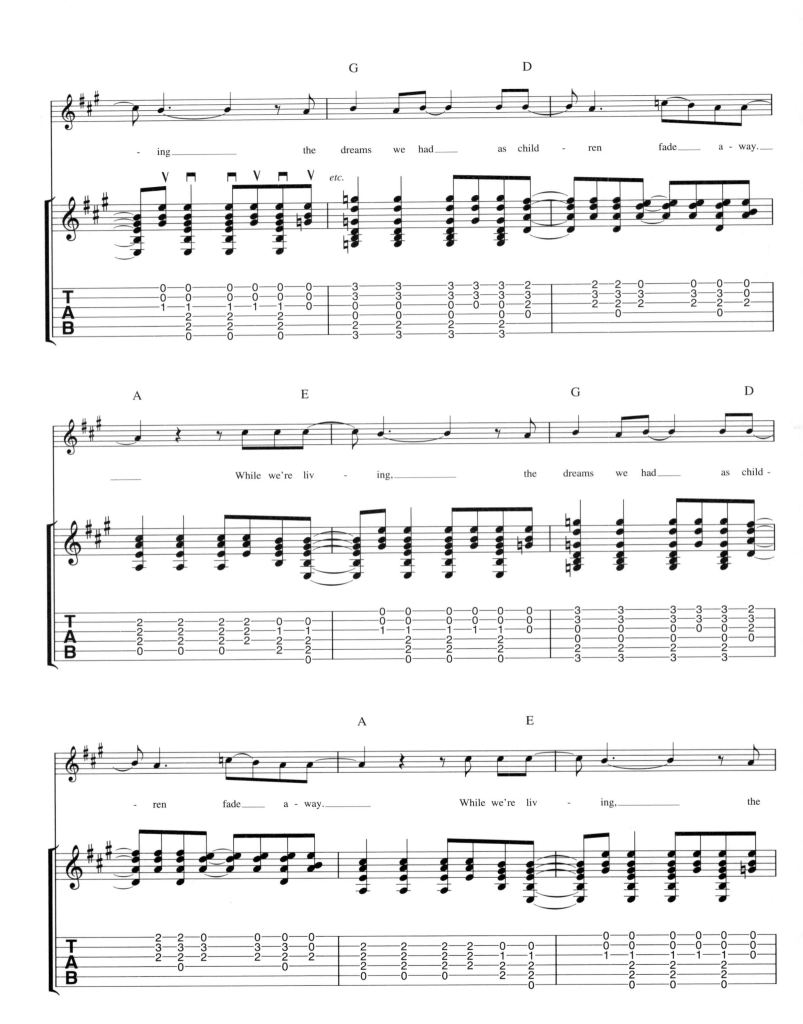

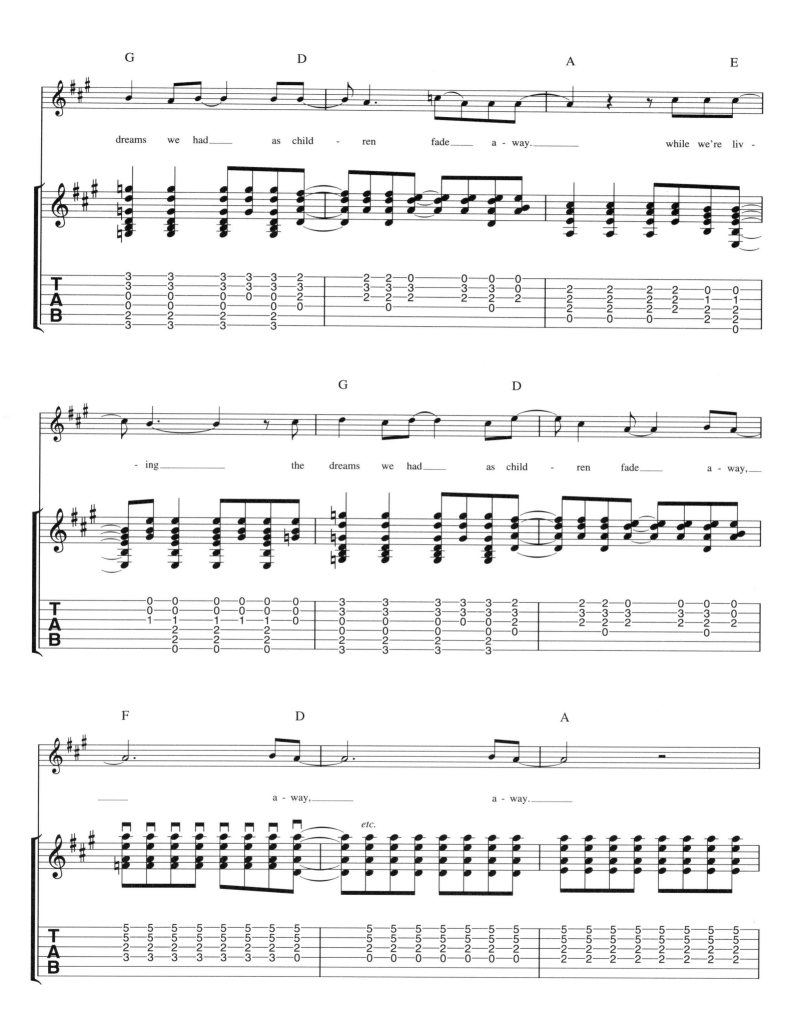

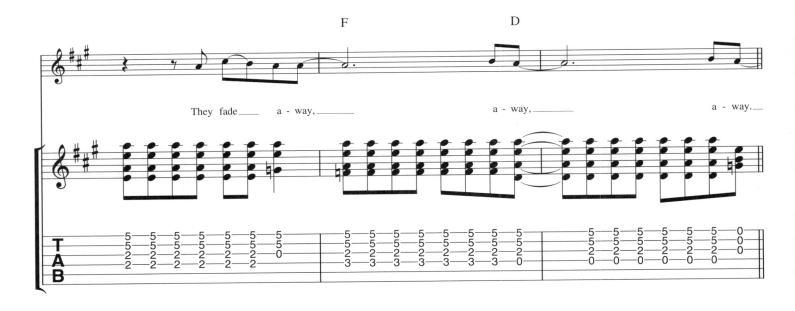

They fade_____ a - way,_____ a - way,_____ a - way._____

1.

Hold shape . . . .

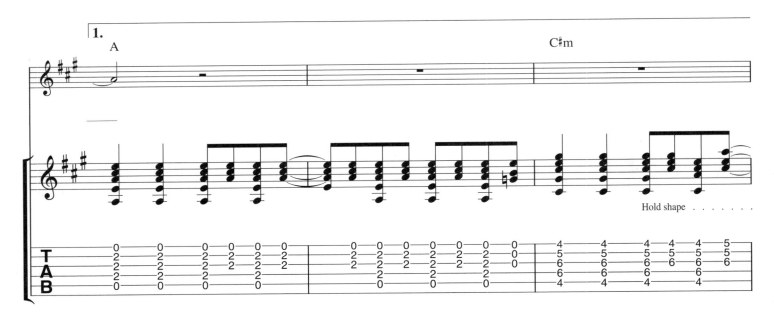

1. cont'd

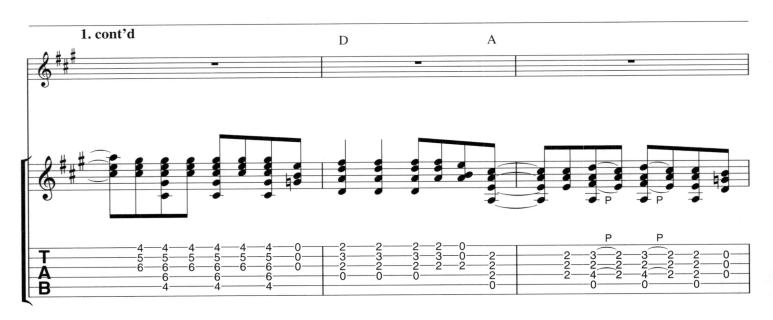

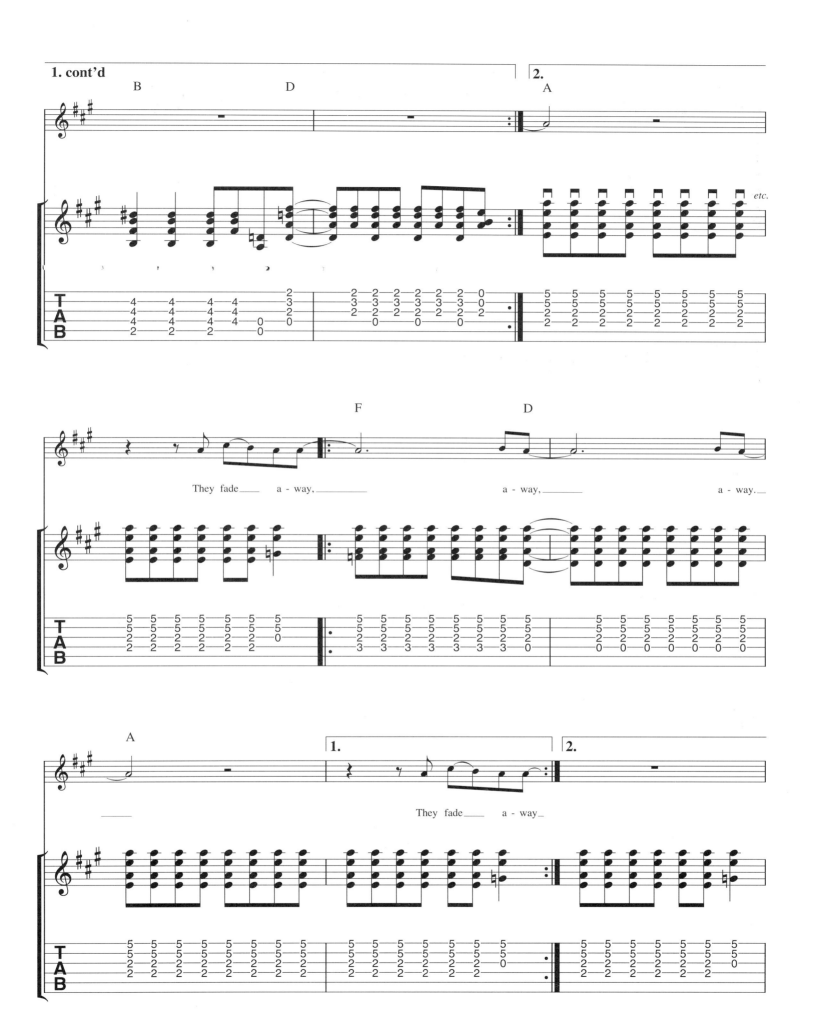

They fade____ a - way,_____ a - way,_____ a - way.____

They fade____ a - way_

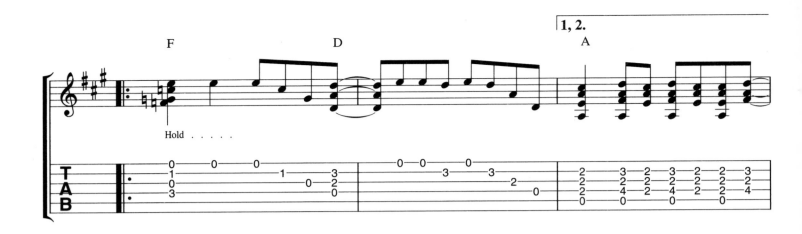

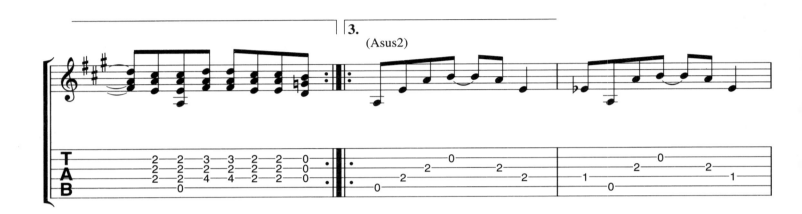

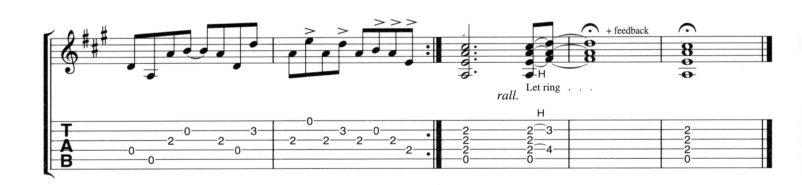

Verse 2: Now my life has turned another corner
I think it's only best that I should warn you
Dream it while you can
Maybe some day I'll make you understand.

(It's Good) To Be Free

Words & Music by Noel Gallagher

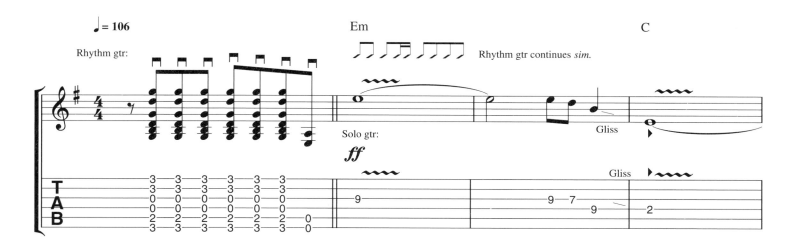

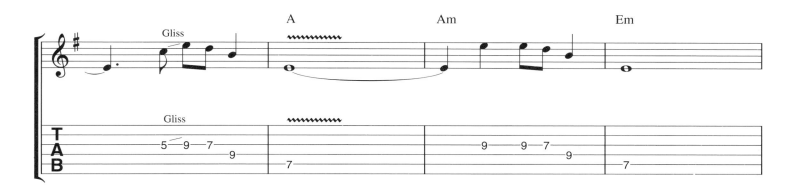

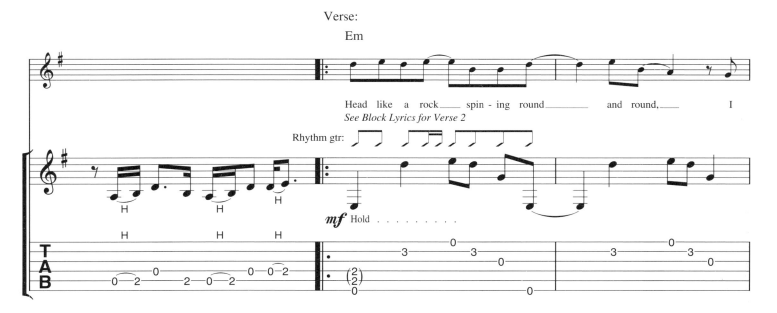

Head like a rock___ spin - ing round___ and round,___ I

See Block Lyrics for Verse 2

found it in___ a hole___ sit - ting up - side down,___ you

sim.

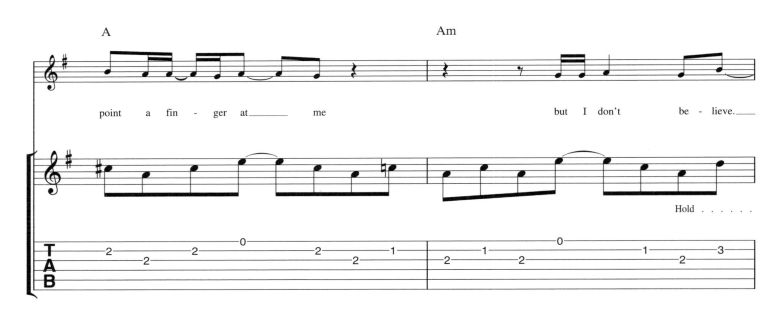

point a fin - ger at___ me but I don't be - lieve.___

Hold . . . . . .

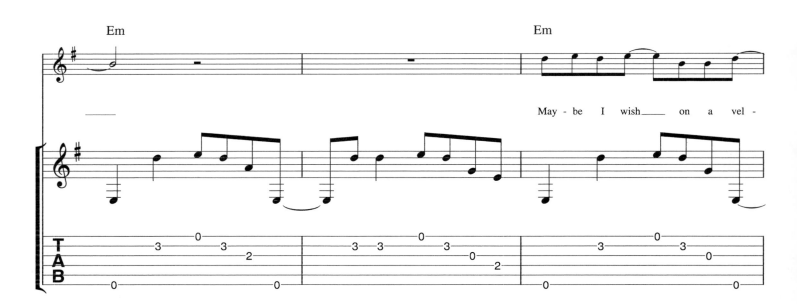

___ May - be I wish___ on a vel -

44

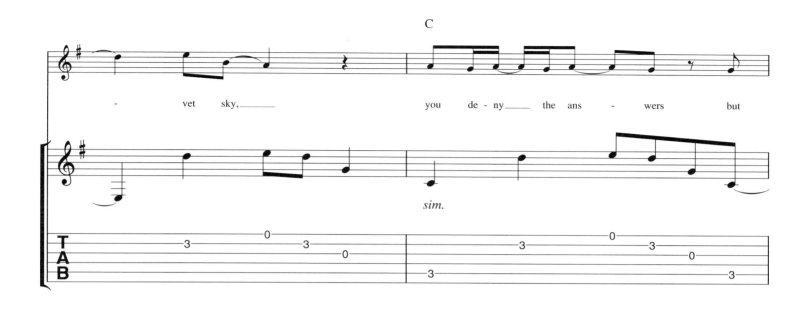

-vet sky,____ you de-ny____ the ans - wers but

sim.

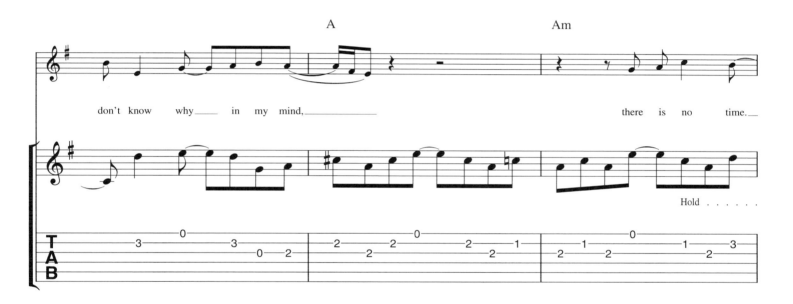

don't know why____ in my mind,____ there is no time.__

Hold . . . . . .

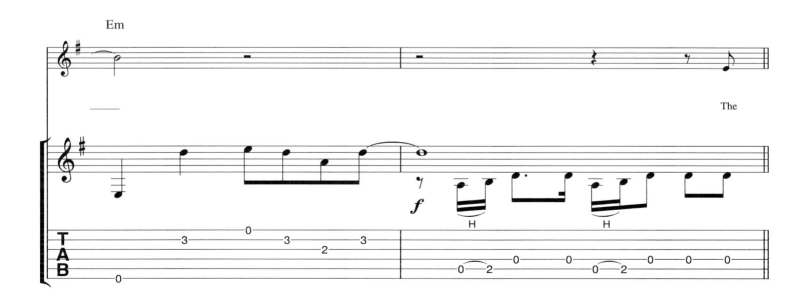

The

Chorus:

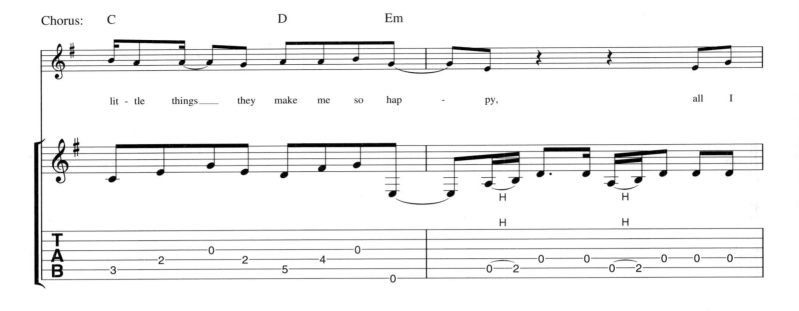

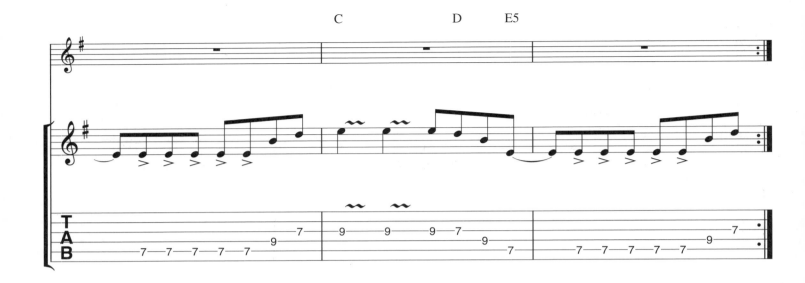

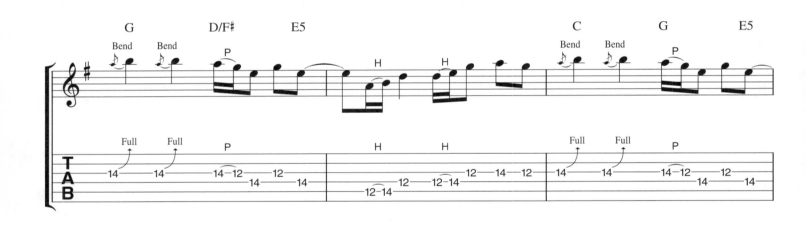

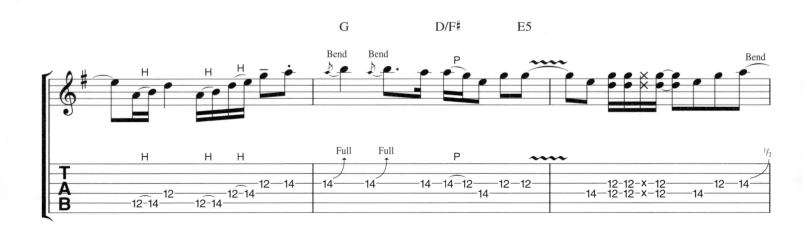

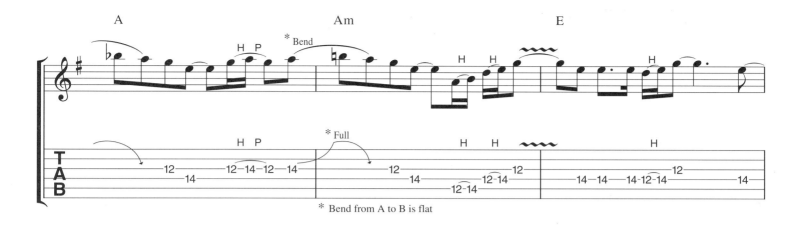

* Bend from A to B is flat

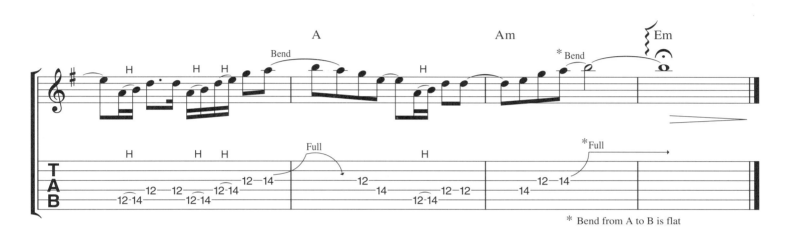

* Bend from A to B is flat

Verse 2:   So what would you say if I said to you
            It's not what you say, it's what you do
            You point your finger at me
            But I don't believe.

            Bring it on home to where we found
            My head is like a rock sitting upside down
            In my mind
            There is no time.

Half The World Away

Words & Music by Noel Gallagher

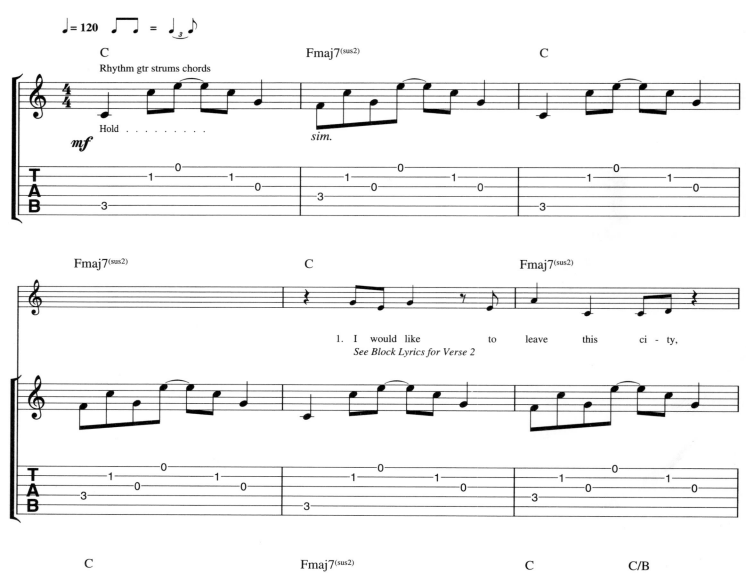

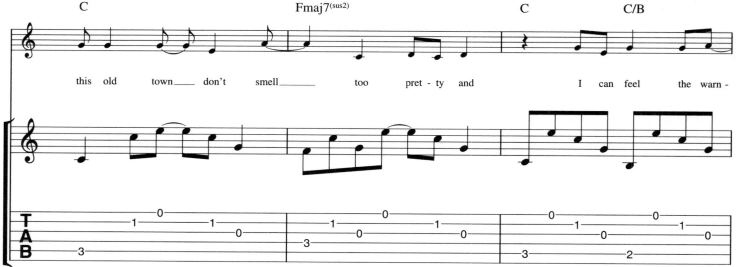

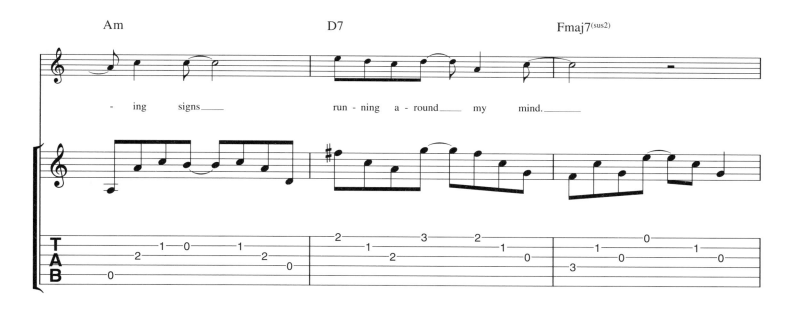

Am D7 Fmaj7^(sus2)

- ing   signs___   run - ning   a - round___   my   mind.___

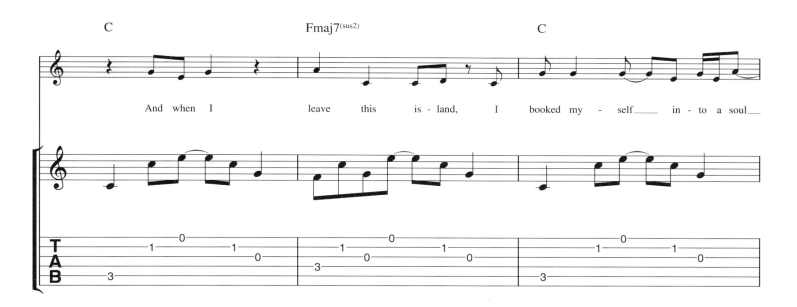

C Fmaj7^(sus2) C

And   when   I   leave   this   is - land,   I   booked   my - self___   in - to   a   soul___

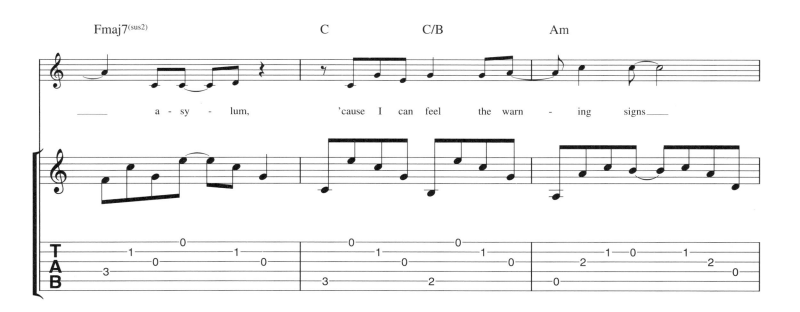

Fmaj7^(sus2) C C/B Am

___   a - sy - lum,   'cause   I   can   feel   the   warn - ing   signs___

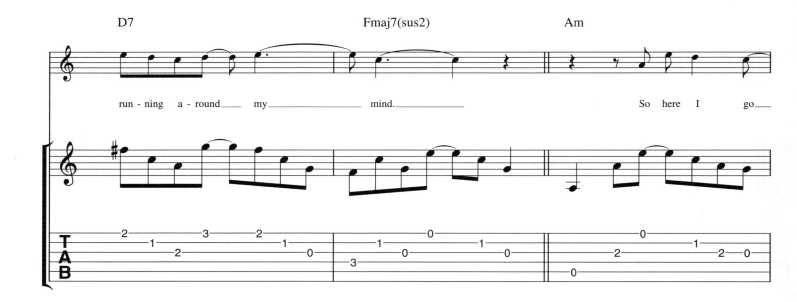

run - ning a - round my mind. So here I go

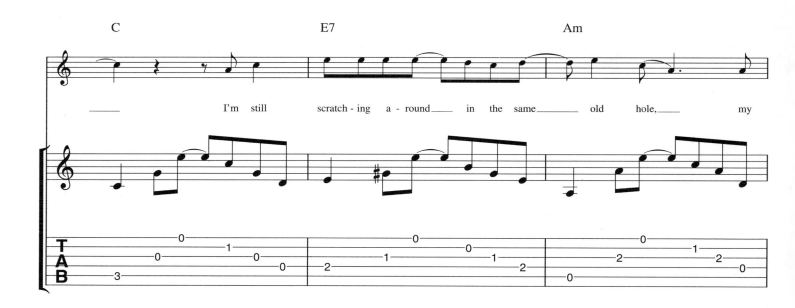

I'm still scratch - ing a - round in the same old hole, my

bo - dy feels young but my mind is ve - ry old.

So what do you say,_____ you can't

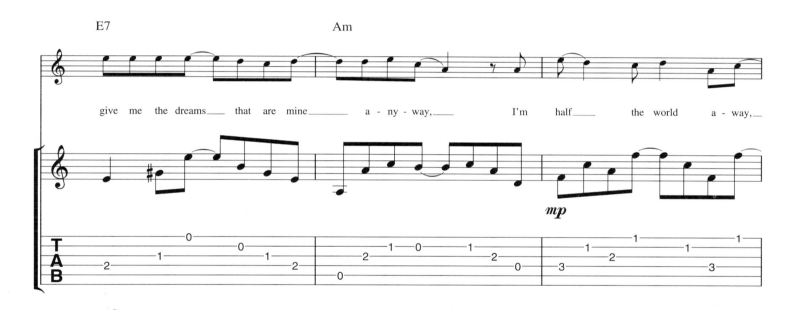

give me the dreams___ that are mine_____ a - ny - way,___ I'm half___ the world a - way,___

mp

half___ the world a - way,_____

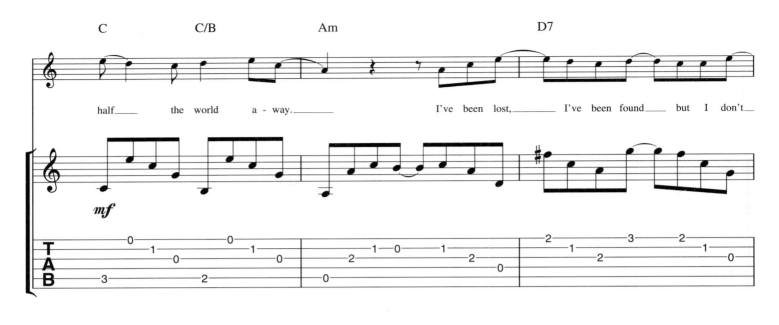

half____ the world a-way.____ I've been lost,____ I've been found____ but I don't____

1.

____ feel down.____

2.

____ feel down.____ No I don't____ feel down,____ no I don't____

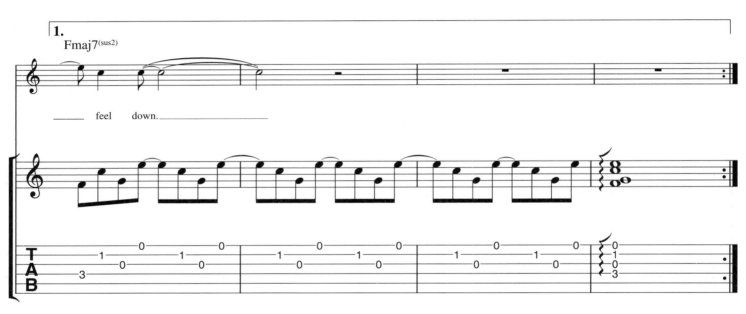

feel   down.___

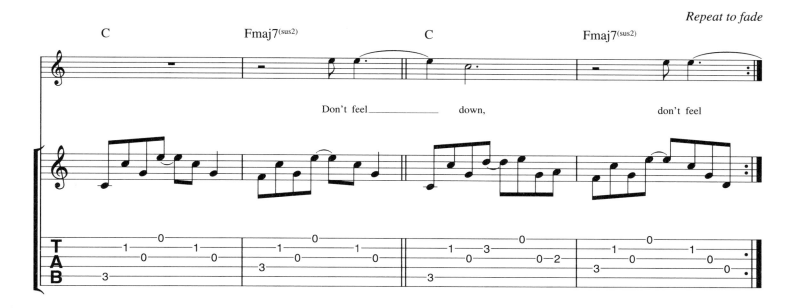

Repeat to fade

C   Fmaj7(sus2)   C   Fmaj7(sus2)

Don't feel_____ down,   don't feel

Verse 2:   And when I leave this planet
You know I'd stay but I just can't stand it
And I can feel the warning signs
Running around my mind.

And if I could leave this spirit
I'd find me a hole and I'll live in it
And I can feel the warning signs
Running around my mind.

Headshrinker

Words & Music by Noel Gallagher

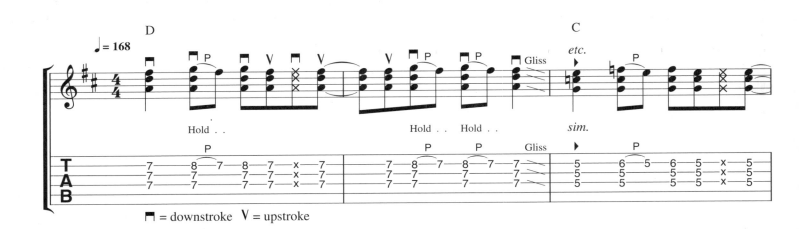

□ = downstroke   V = upstroke

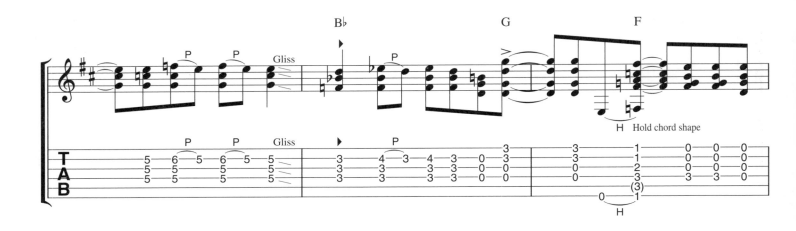

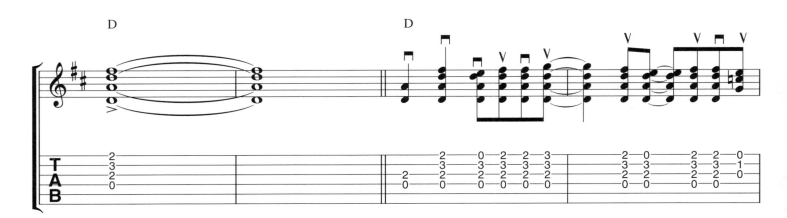

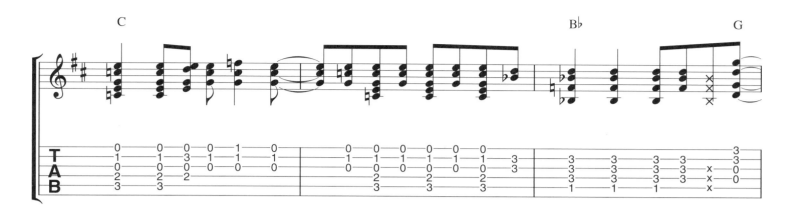

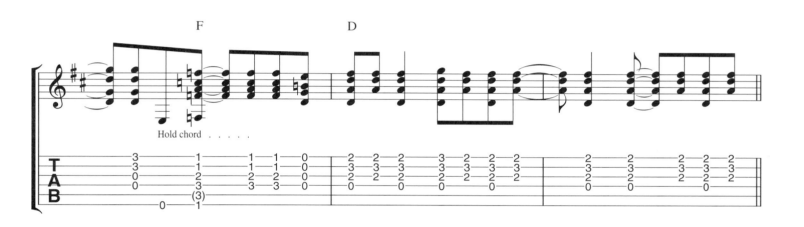

Verse:

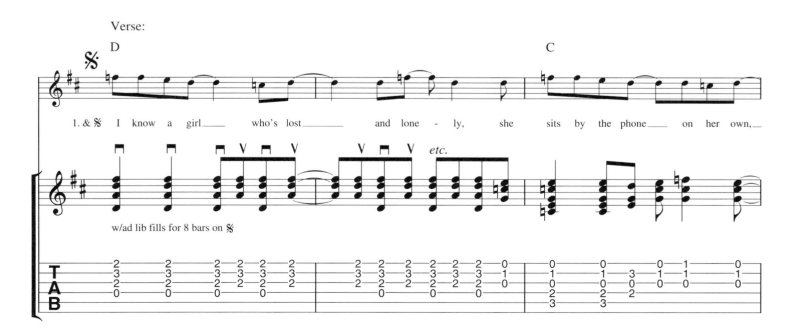

1. & 𝄋 I know a girl___ who's lost___ and lone-ly, she sits by the phone___ on her own,___

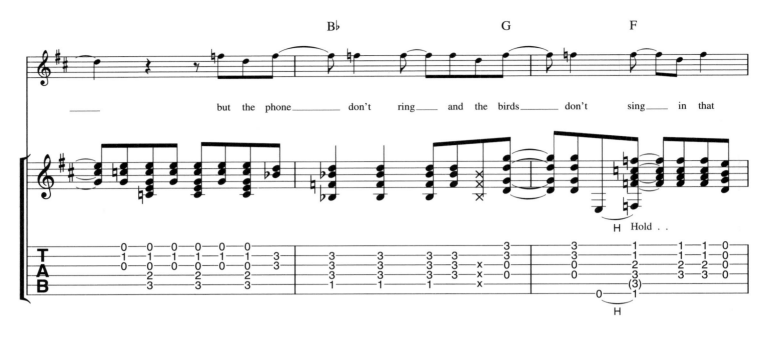

but the phone_____ don't ring_____ and the birds_____ don't sing_____ in that

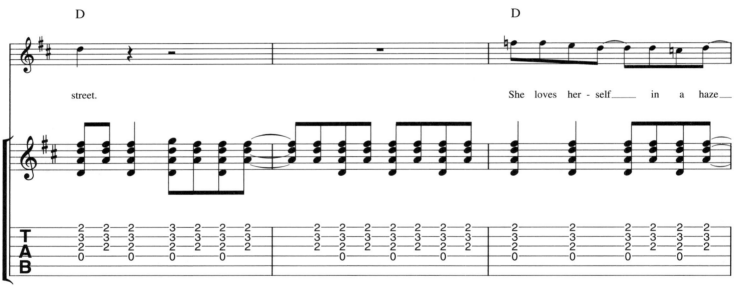

street.

She loves her-self_____ in a haze_____

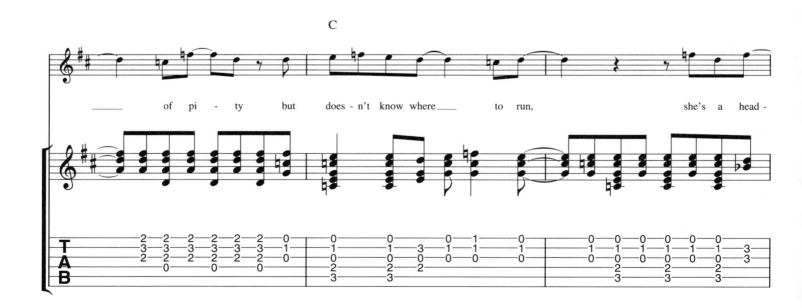

_____ of pi - ty but does - n't know where_____ to run, she's a head-

for the rest of your_____ lives._____

For the rest of your

lives.

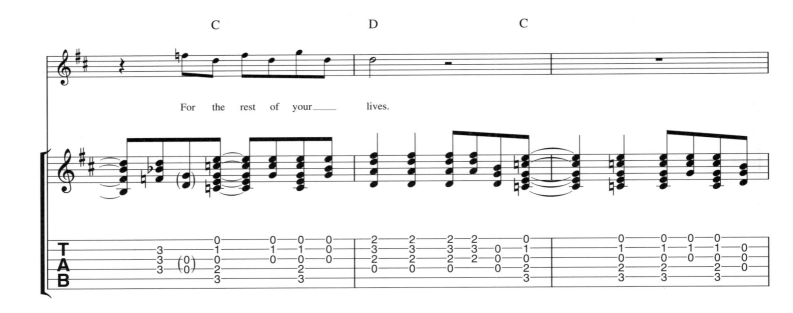

For the rest of your____ lives.

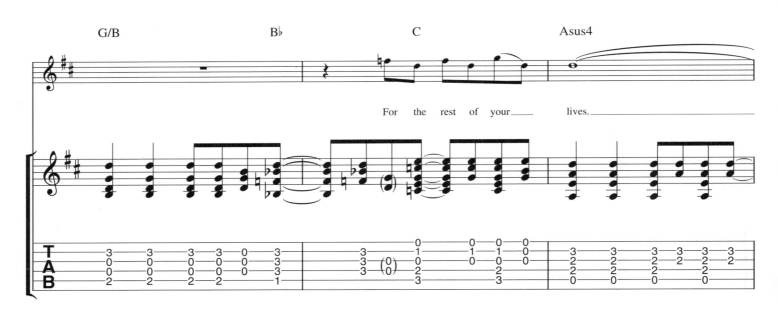

For the rest of your____ lives.____

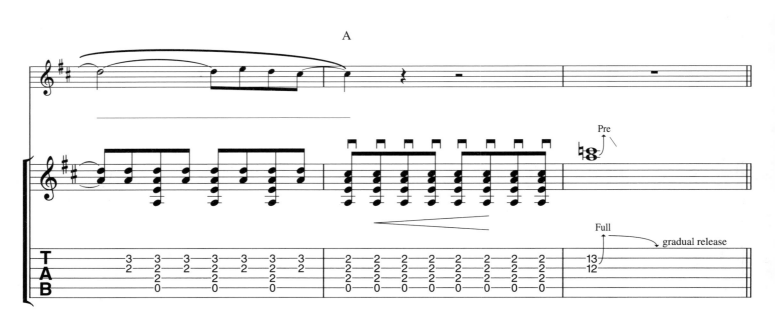

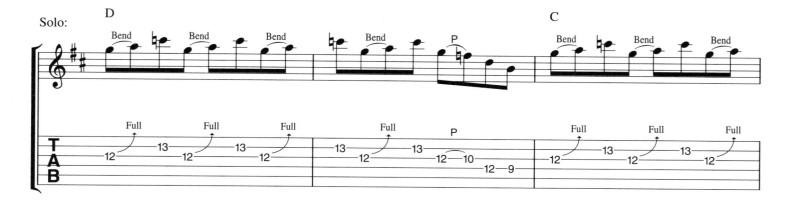

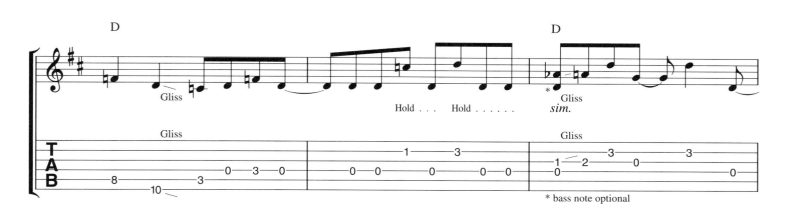

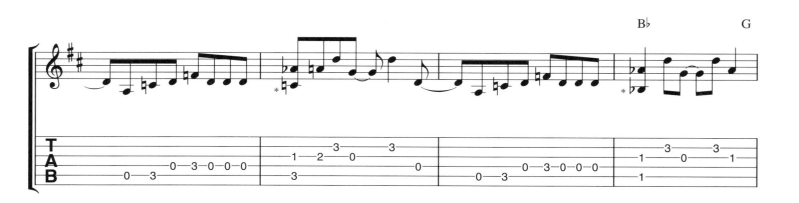

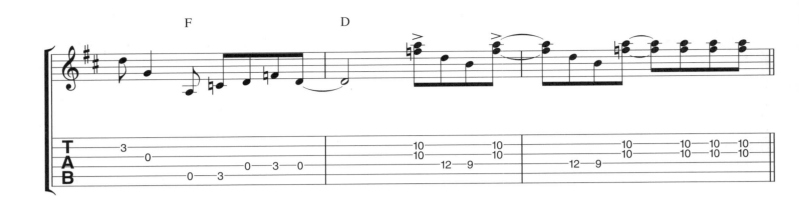

Lost in the fog___ of the ci - ty like a dog and I'm out - ta here.

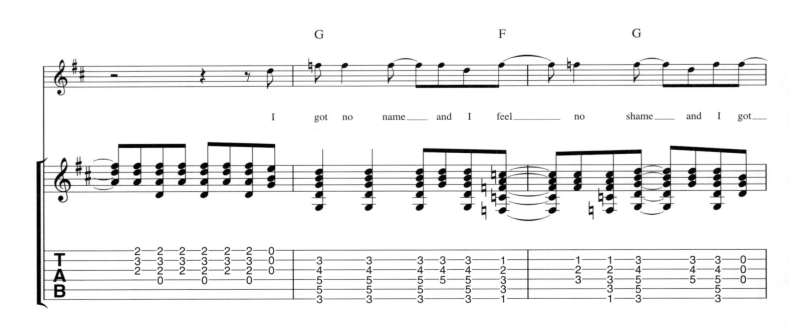

I got no name___ and I feel_____ no shame___ and I got___

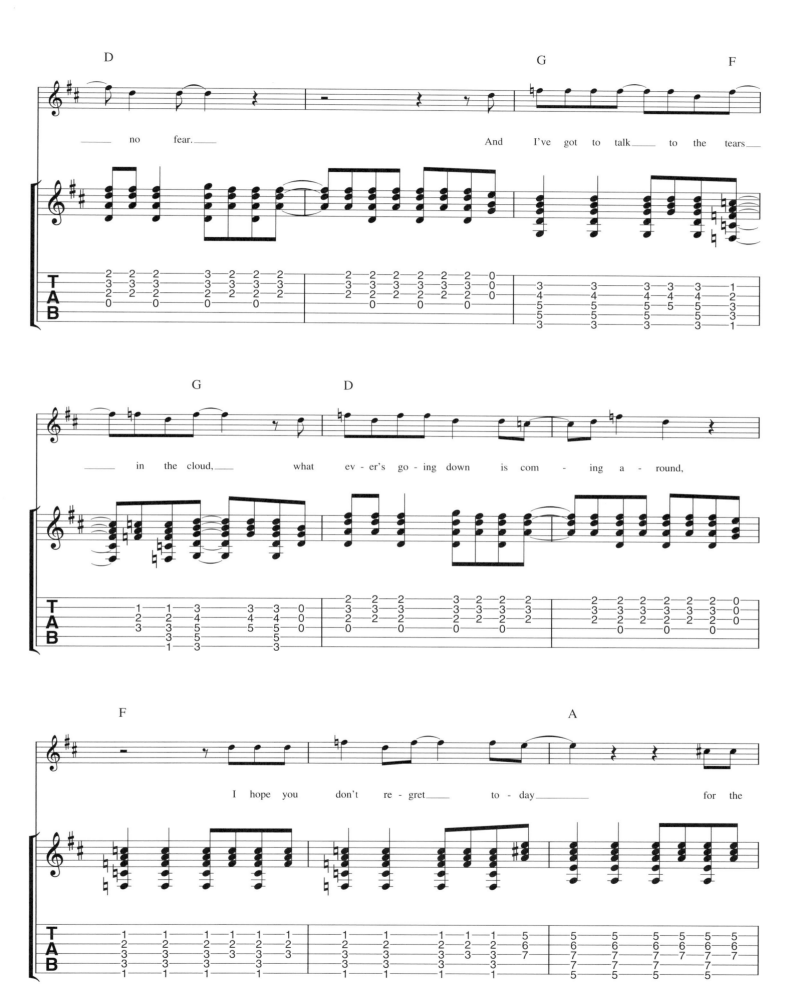

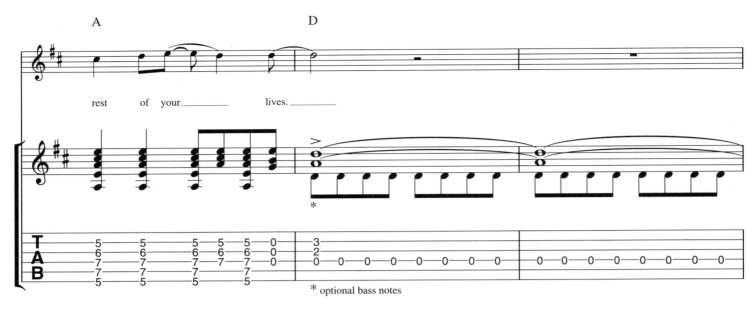

rest   of   your_____   lives._____

* optional bass notes

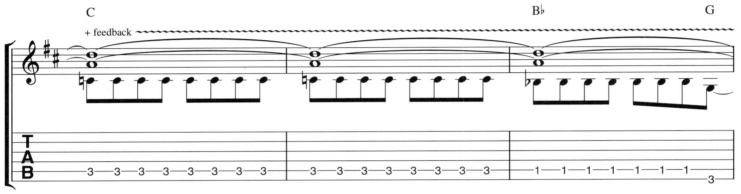

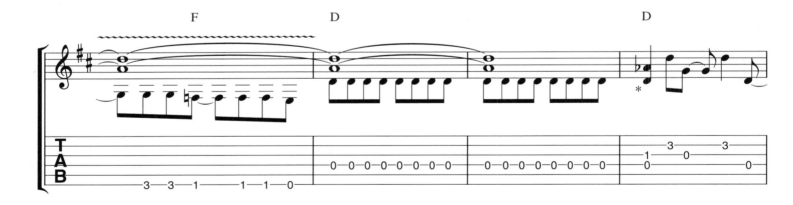

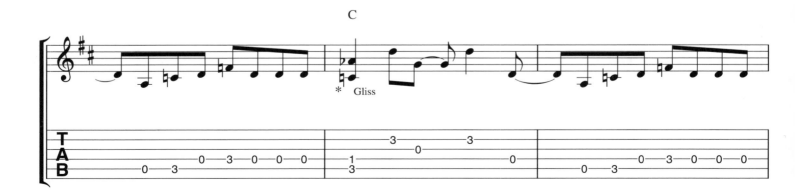

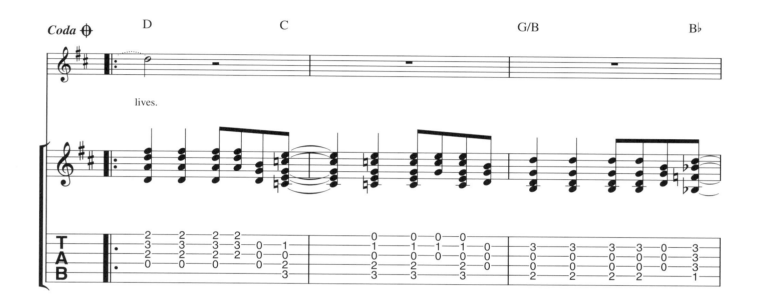

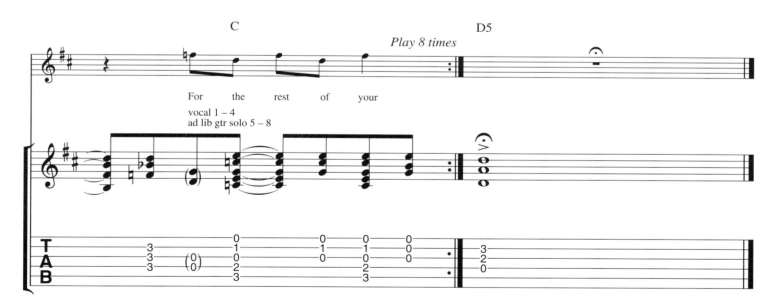

It's Better People

Words & Music by Noel Gallagher

= 110

Capo 2nd fret

hit gtr sound board!

Fig 1. . . . (Gtr 2 plays rhythm as per verse)

1, 3.

F#m7 A

. . . Fig 1. ends

4.

F#m7 A

1. 2. It's

Verse: E Bsus4 F#m7 A

bet - ter peo - ple love one an - oth - er, 'cause liv - ing a life___ can be

etc.

⊓ = downstroke V = upstroke

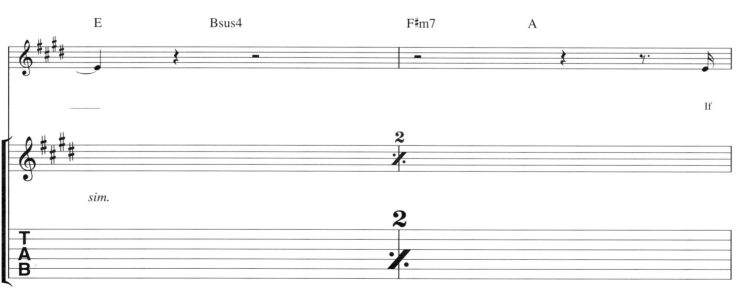

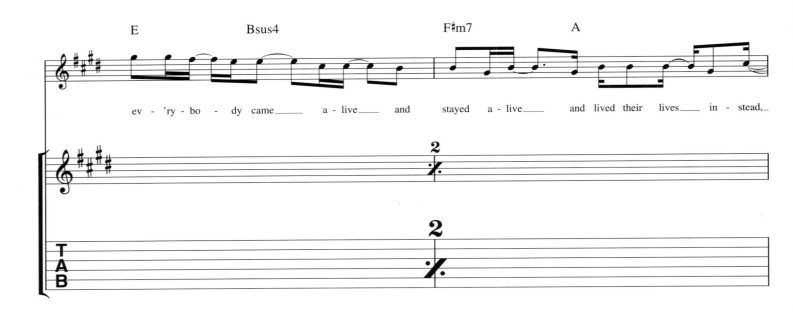

ev - 'ry - bo - dy came___ a - live___ and stayed a - live___ and lived their lives___ in - stead,___

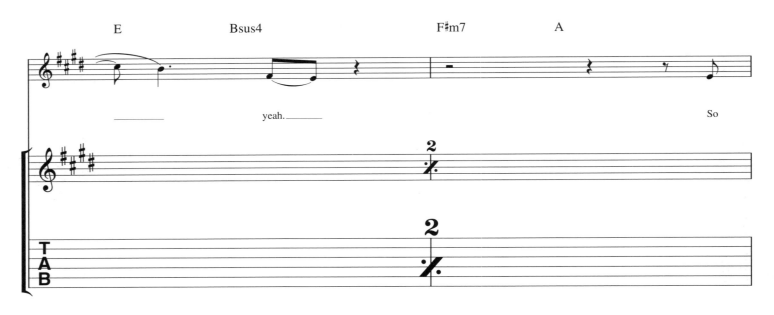

___ ___ yeah.___ So

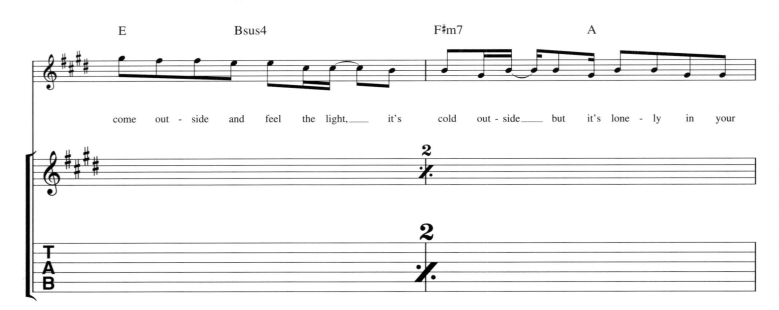

come out - side and feel the light,___ it's cold out - side___ but it's lone - ly in your

bed,   in   your   bed.

Now you thought we might   be,   what   you   heard be -

etc.

fore   was on - ly sleep - ing in_____ your   brain.

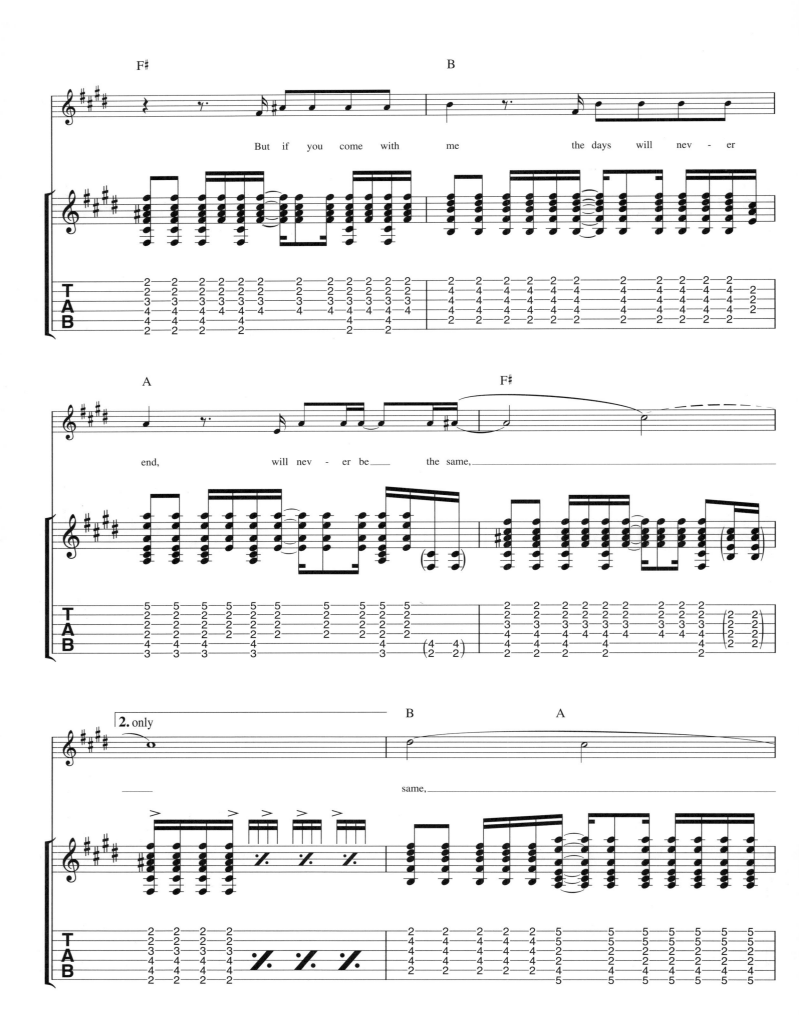

But if you come with me   the days will nev - er

end,   will nev - er be____ the same,_____

2. only

____   same,_____

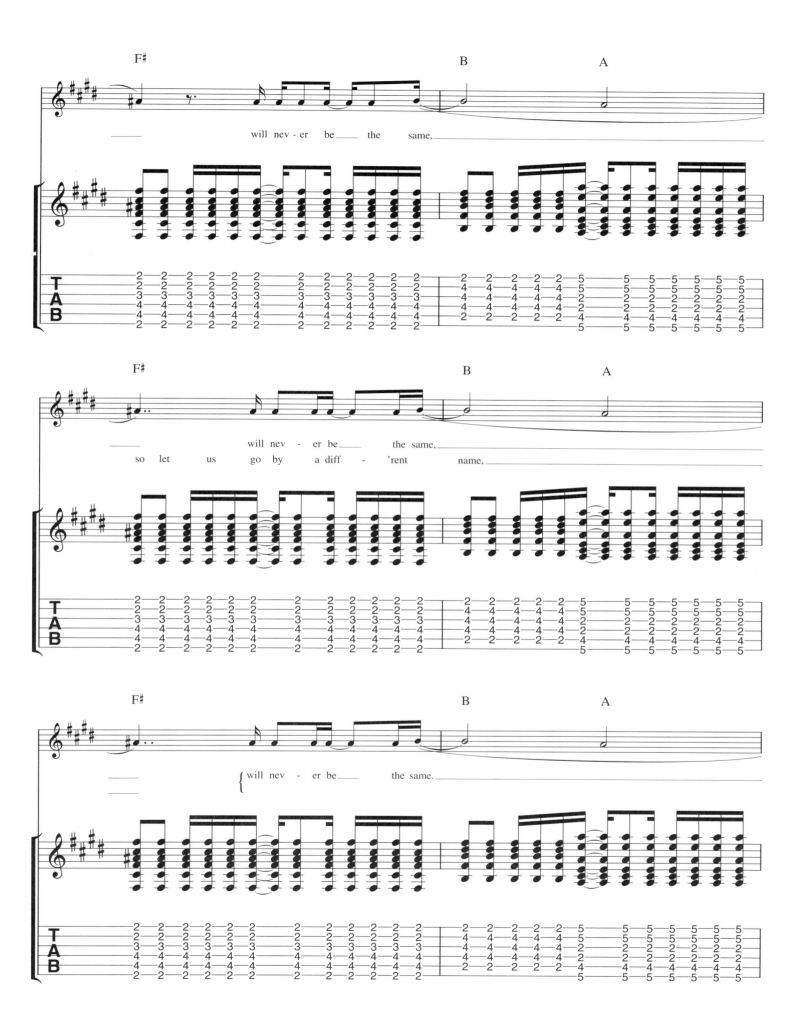

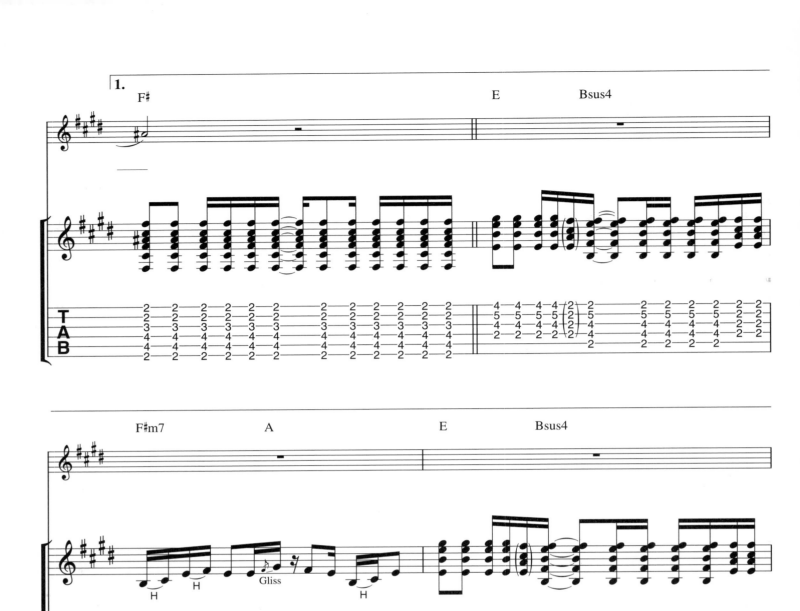

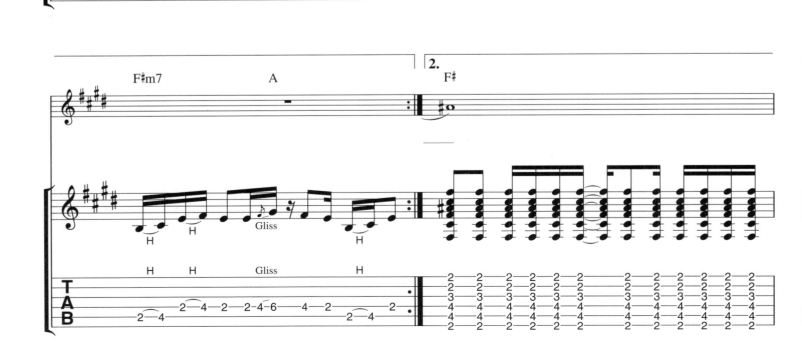

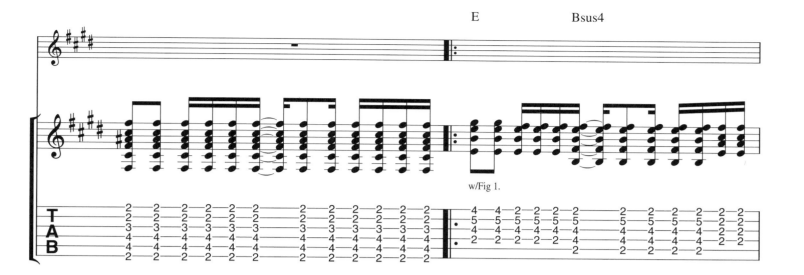

w/Fig 1.

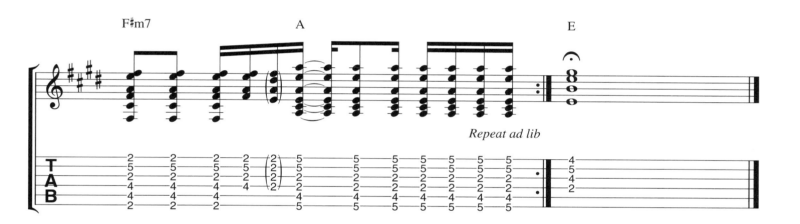

Repeat ad lib

I Will Believe

Words & Music by Noel Gallagher

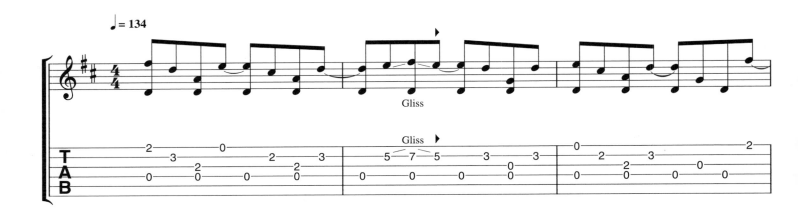

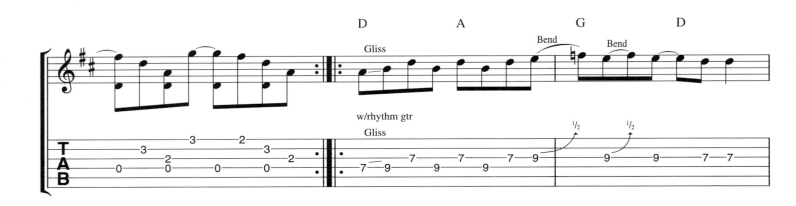

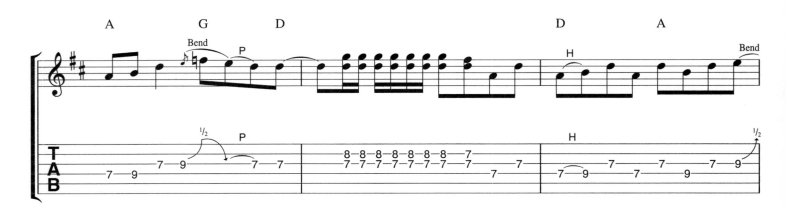

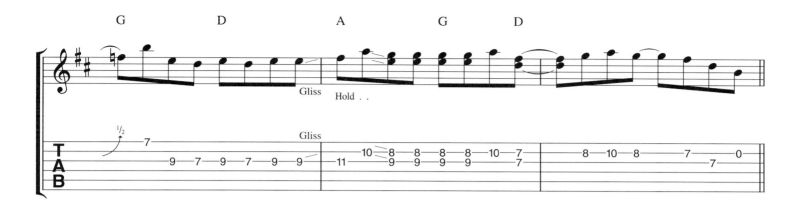

Verse:

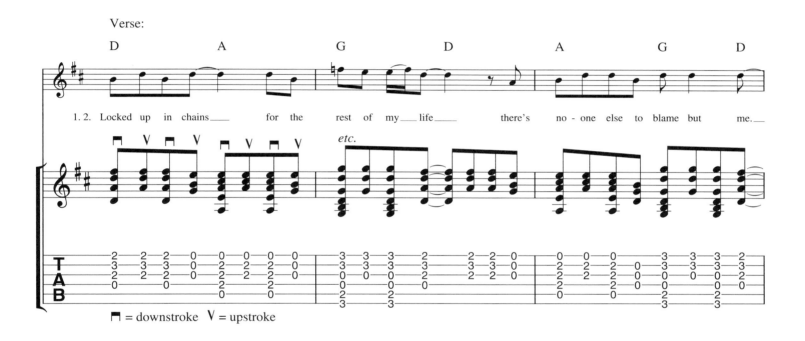

1. 2. Locked up in chains____ for the rest of my____ life____ there's no - one else to blame but me.____

☐ = downstroke V = upstroke

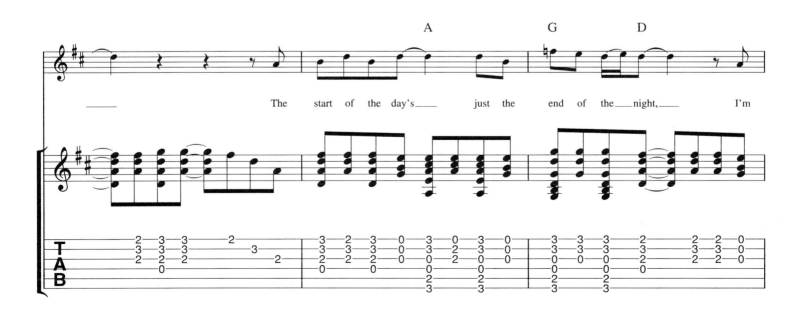

____ The start of the day's____ just the end of the____ night,____ I'm

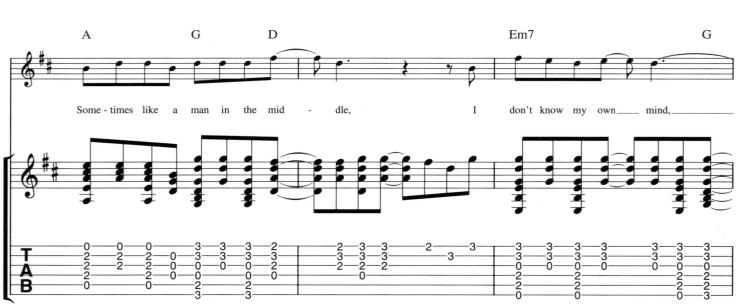

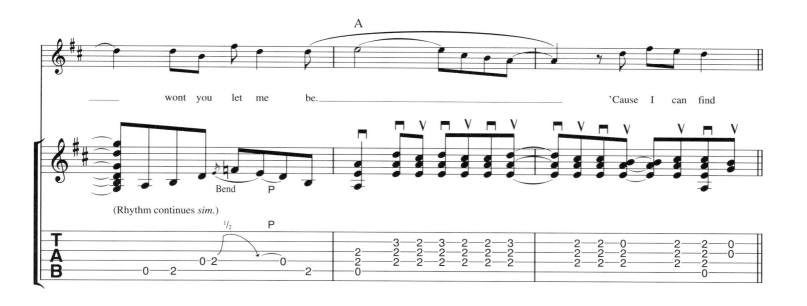

A

wont you let me be._____ 'Cause I can find

(Rhythm continues *sim.*)

Chorus:

D   Cadd9   A7   D

you liv-ing in my____ world drag-ging me round____ just like a dog on a lead____

Hold chord . . . . . . *sim.*

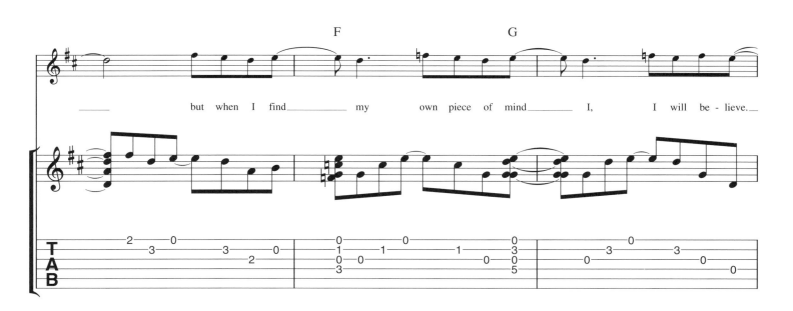

F   G

____ but when I find____ my own piece of mind____ I, I will be-lieve.____

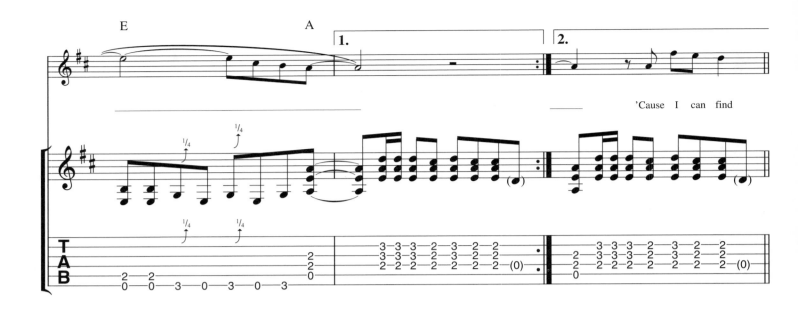

'Cause I can find

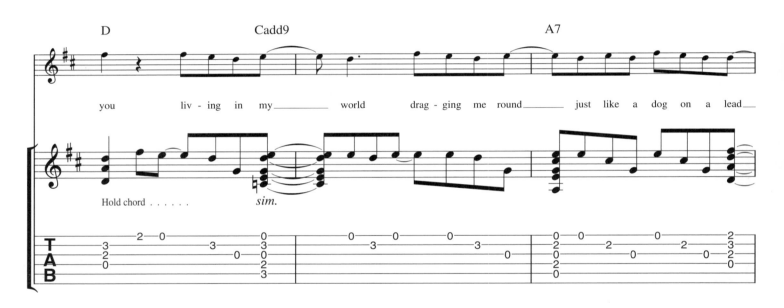

you liv - ing in my____ world   drag - ging me round____ just like a dog on a lead____

Hold chord . . . . . .   *sim.*

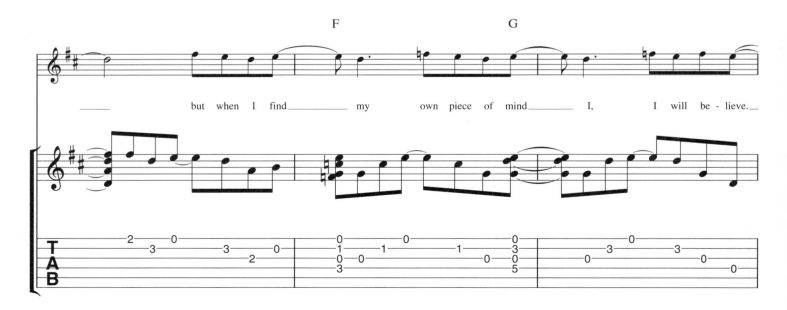

____ but when I find_____ my   own piece of mind ____ I,   I will be - lieve.

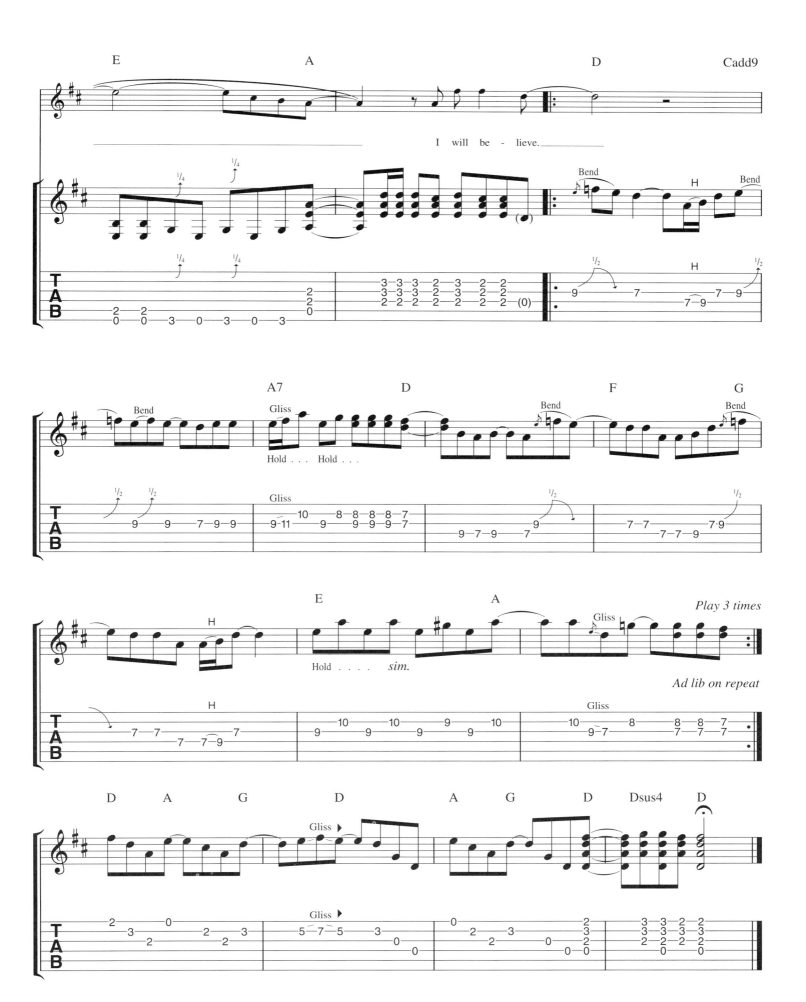

I will be - lieve.

Listen Up

Words & Music by Noel Gallagher

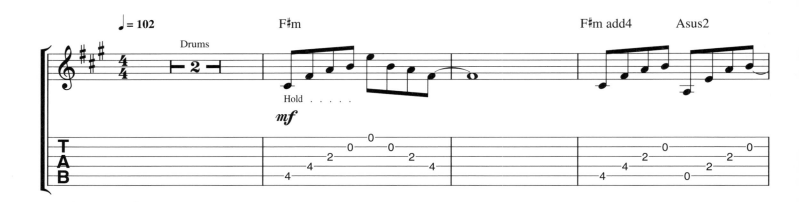

Verse:

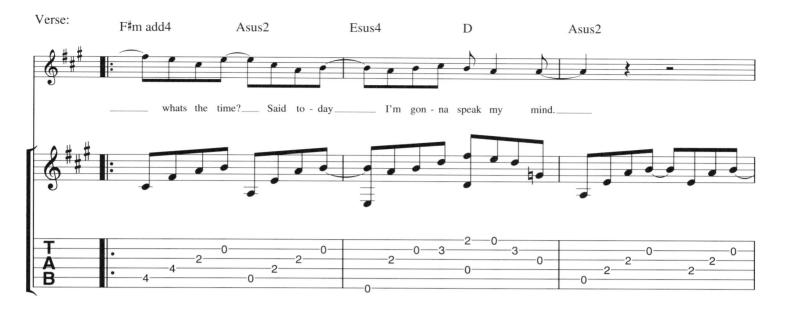

_____ whats the time?_____ Said to-day_____ I'm gon-na speak my   mind._____

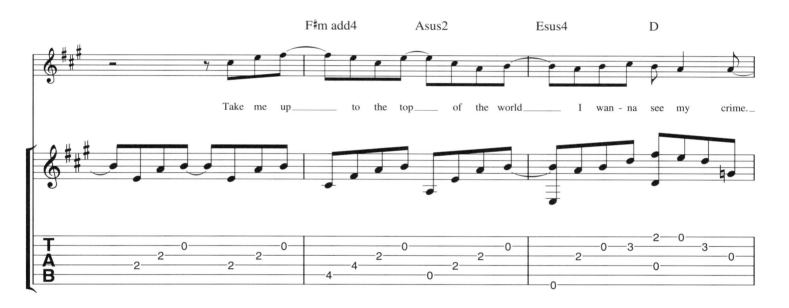

Take me up_____ to the top_____ of the world_____ I wan-na see my   crime.____

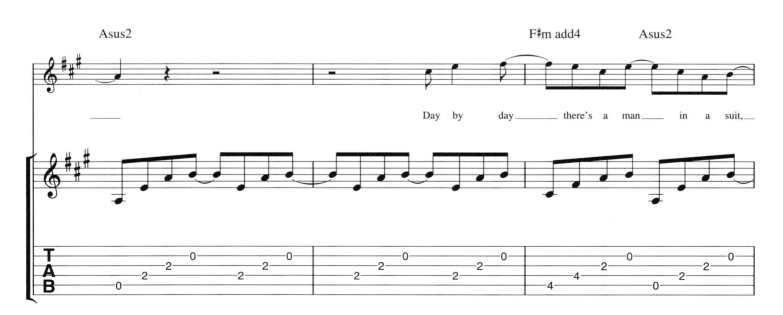

_____ Day by   day_____ there's a man_____ in a   suit,____

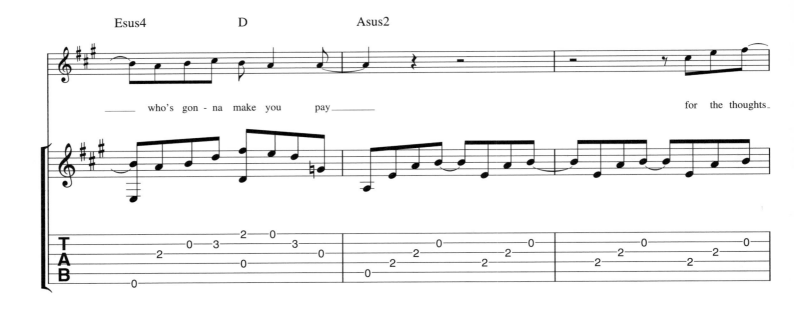

who's gon - na make you pay _____

for the thoughts _

that you think ____ and the words _____ they won't ____ let you say. _____

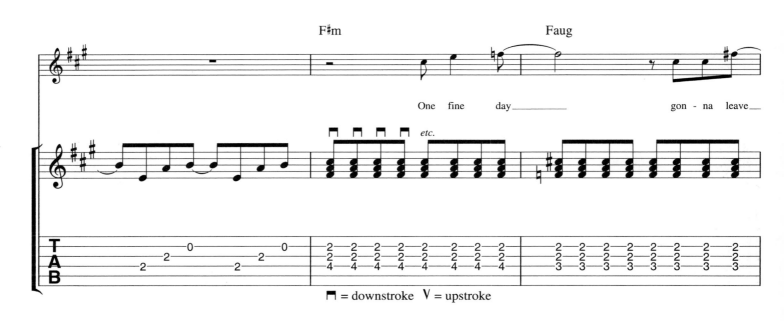

One fine day _____

gon - na leave _

⊓ = downstroke V = upstroke

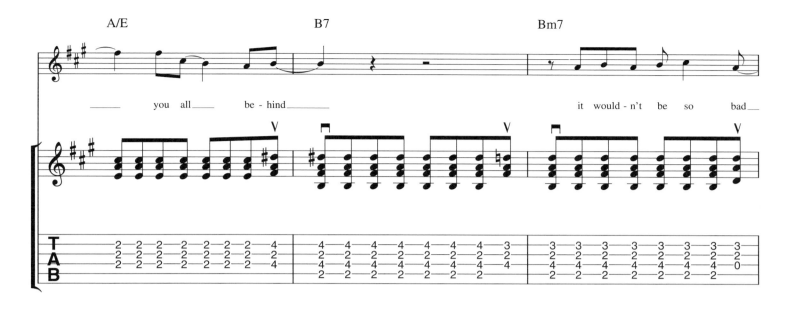

you all____ be - hind_____   it would - n't be so bad___

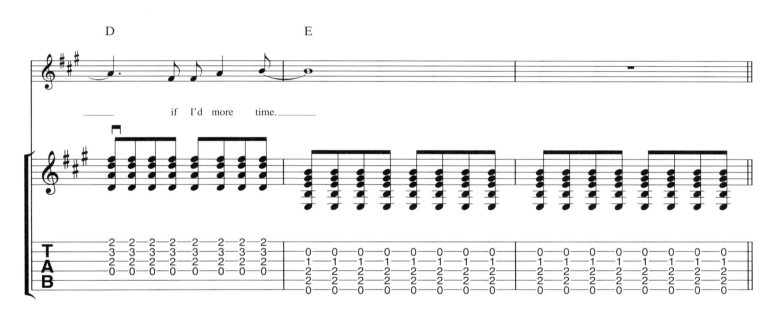

if I'd more time._____

Chorus:

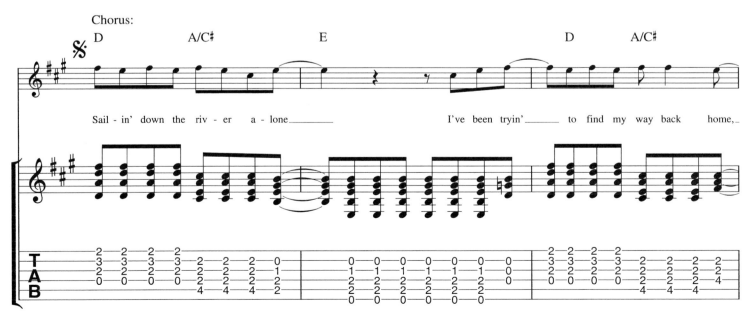

Sail - in' down the riv - er a - lone_____   I've been tryin'_____ to find my way back   home,_

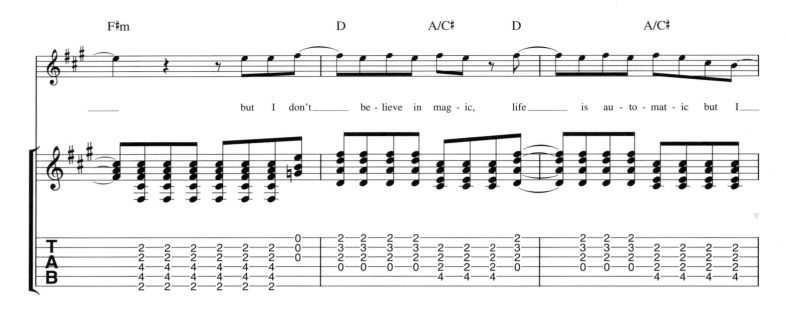

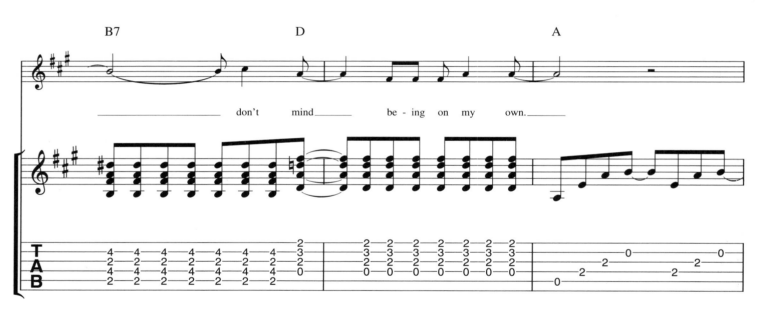

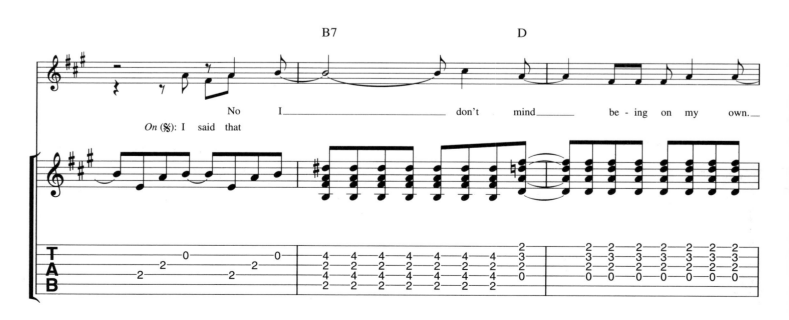

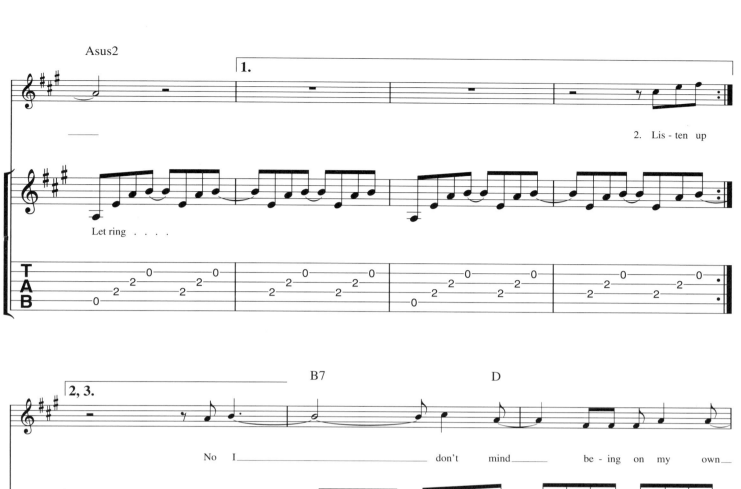

Asus2

1.

Let ring . . . .

2. Lis - ten up

2, 3.

B7

D

No I_____ don't mind_____ be - ing on my own_____

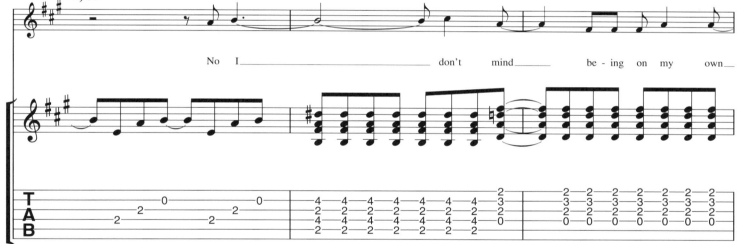

Asus2

B7

I said that I_____ don't mind_____

Let ring . . . . . .

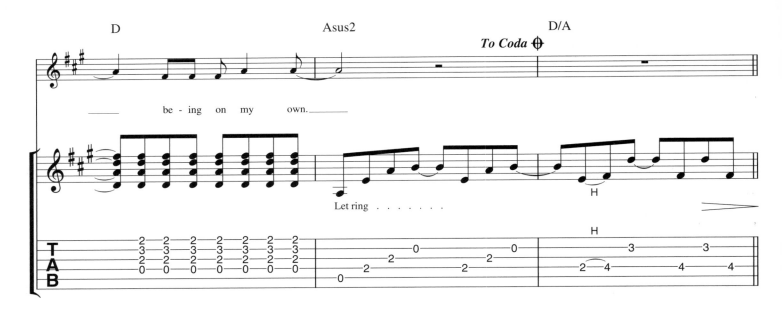

be - ing on my own.

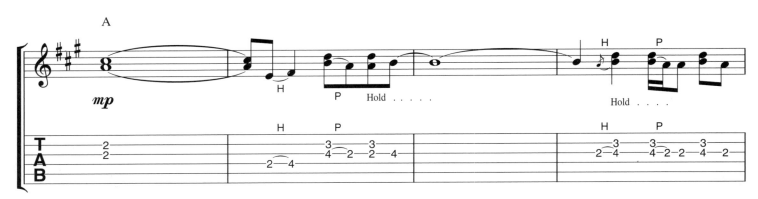

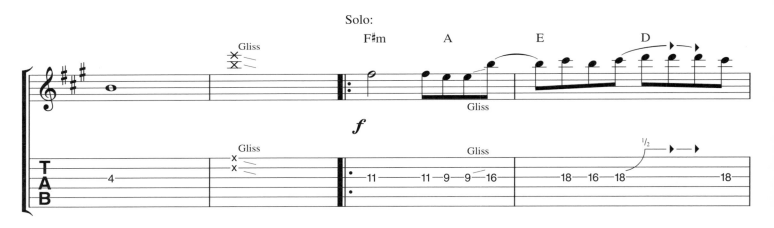

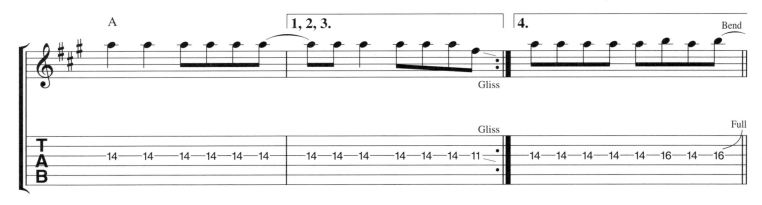

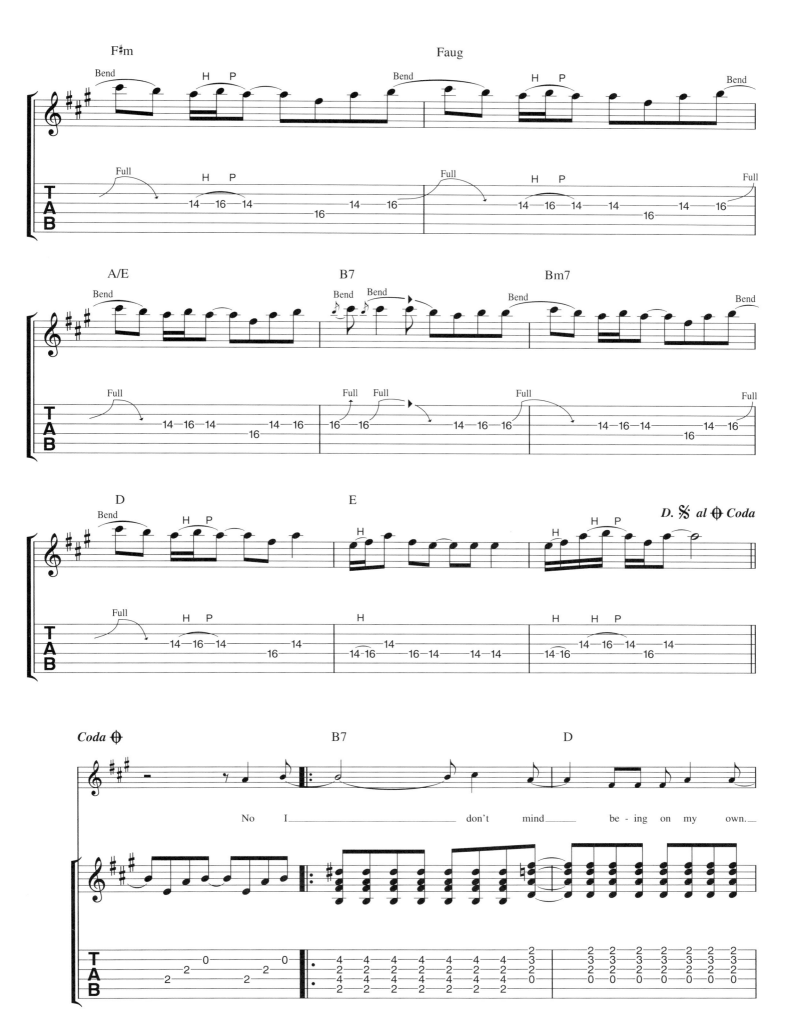

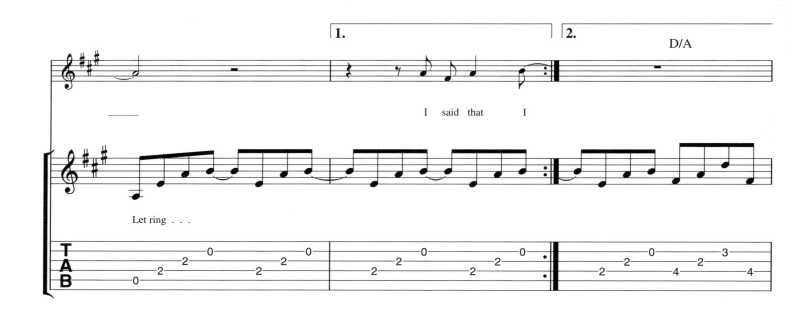

I said that I

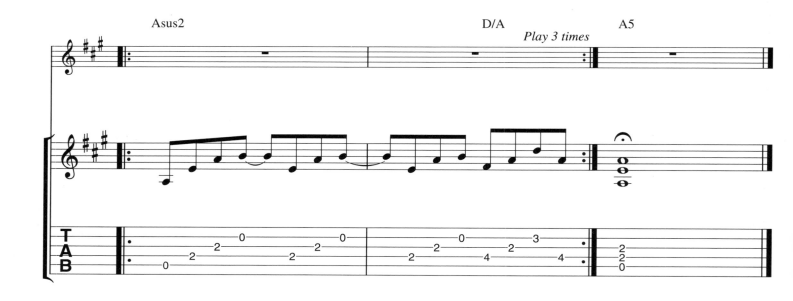

Take Me Away

Words & Music by Noel Gallagher

Verse:

1. Just when it falls___ a - part___

2. Instrumental (8 bars)

Hold . . . . . . *sim.*

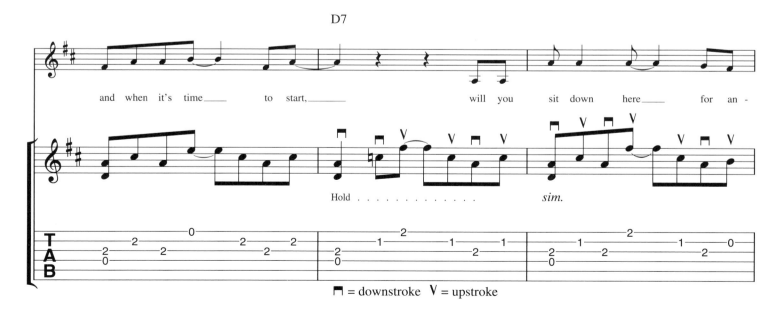

and when it's time___ to start,___ will you sit down here___ for an -

Hold . . . . *sim.*

⊓ = downstroke V = upstroke

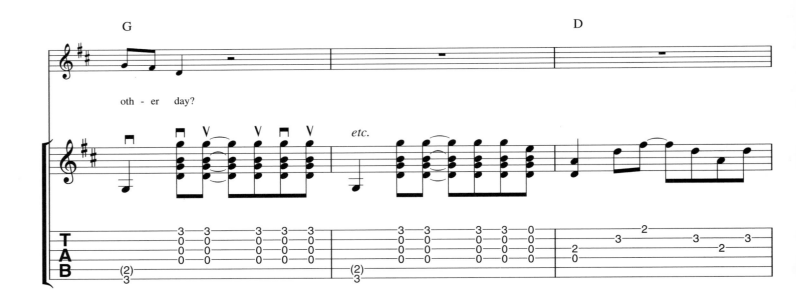

oth - er day?

And when it's time___ to be,___ all the things___ that we___

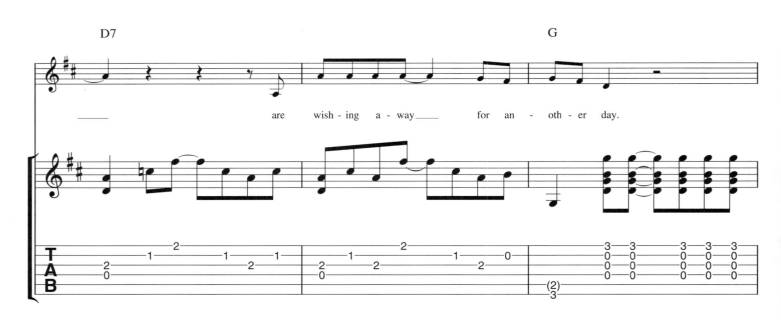

___ are wish - ing a - way___ for an - oth - er day.

92

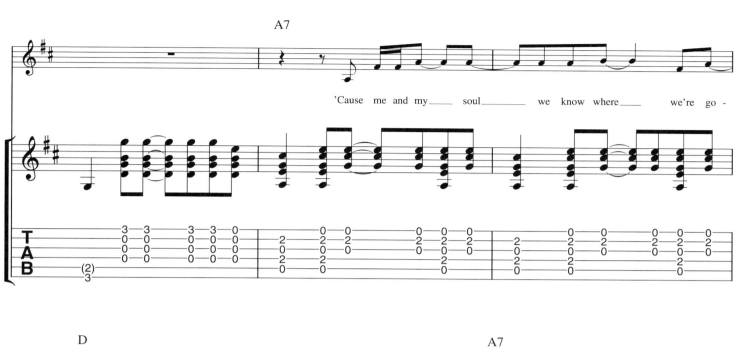

'Cause me and my____ soul____ we know where____ we're go -

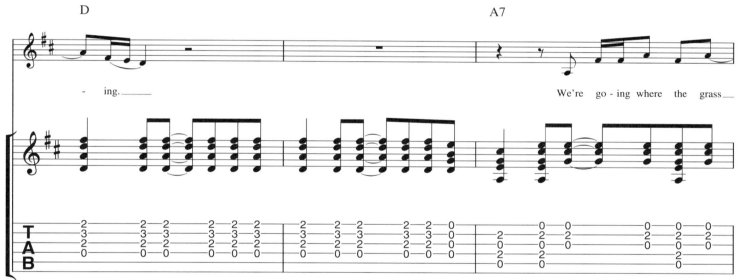

- ing.____ We're go-ing where the grass____

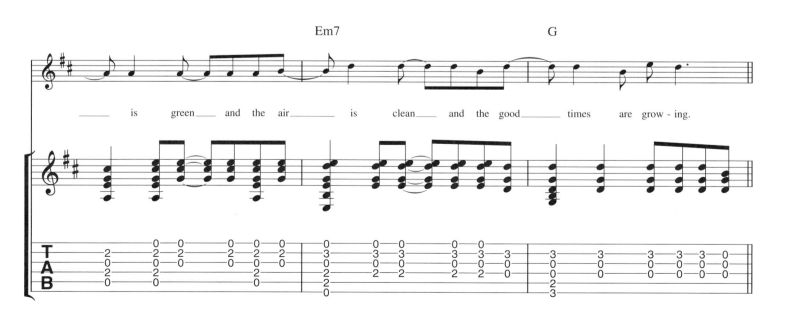

____ is green____ and the air____ is clean____ and the good____ times are grow-ing.

93

Chorus:

94

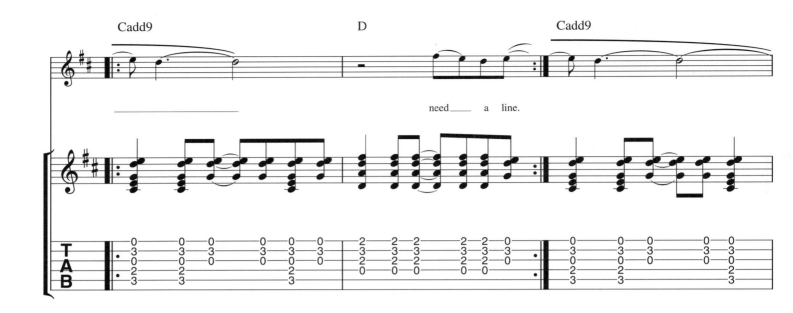

need___ a line.

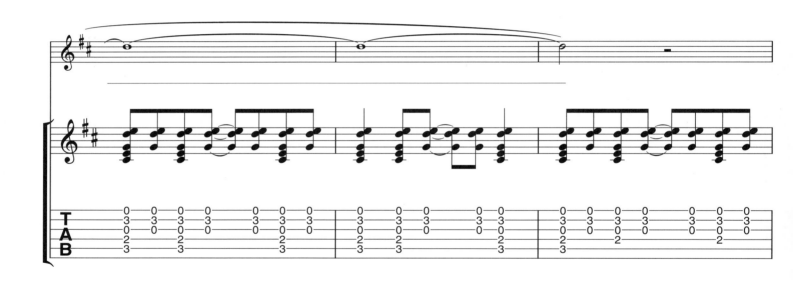

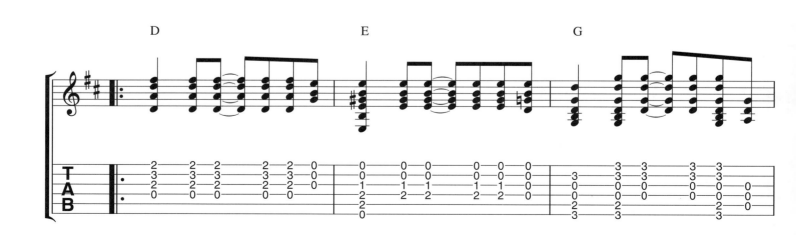

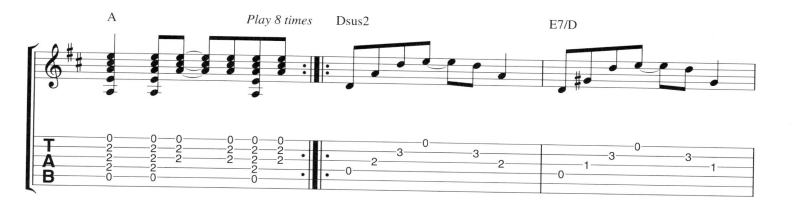

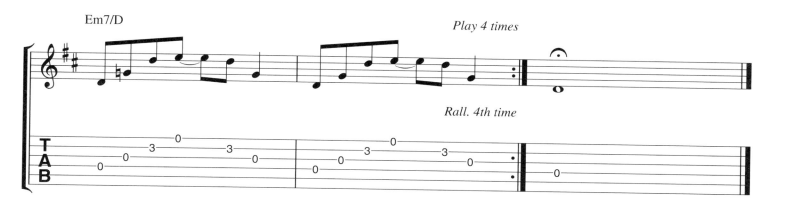

Verse 2:   *Instrumental 8 bars*
And just when it falls apart
And just when it's time to start
Will you sit down here for another day?

Rockin' Chair

Words & Music by Noel Gallagher

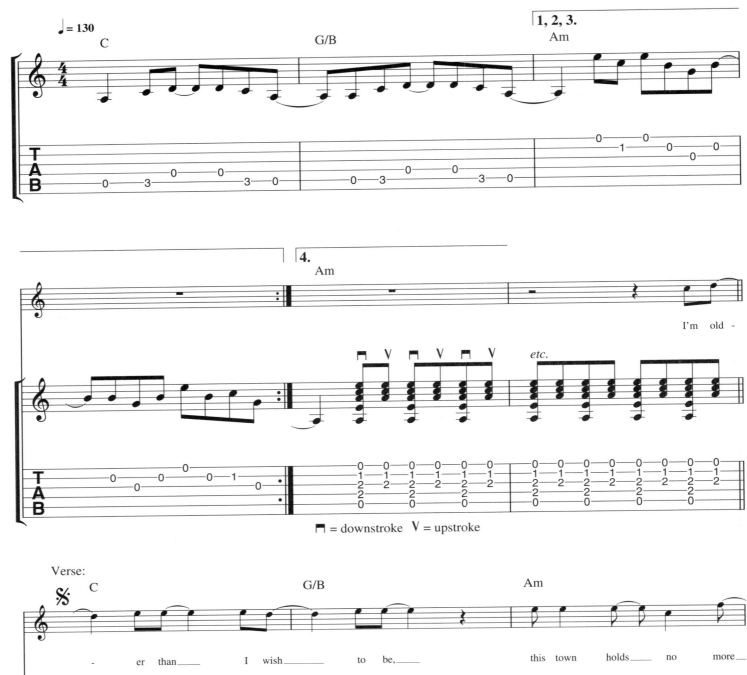

= downstroke V = upstroke

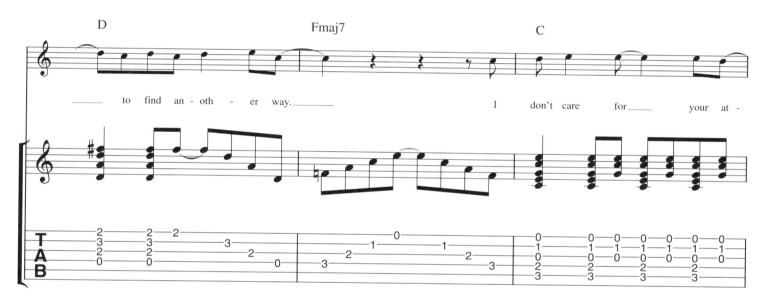

All my life I've tried to make a bet - ter day.

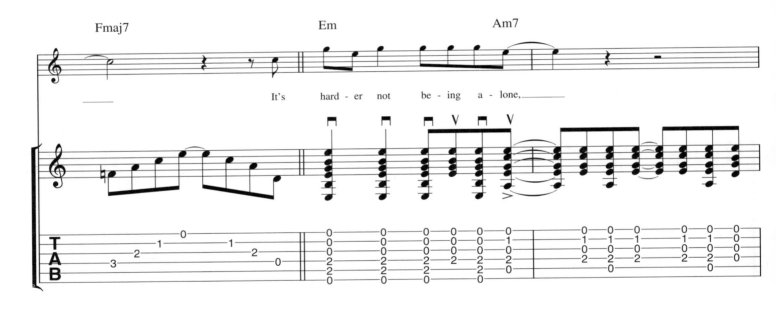

It's hard - er not be - ing a - lone,

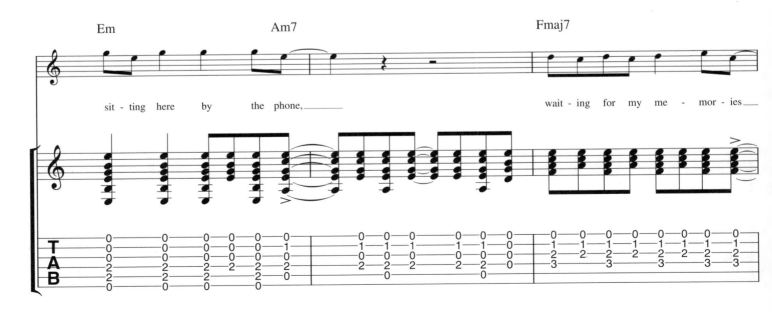

sit - ting here by the phone, wait - ing for my me - mor - ies

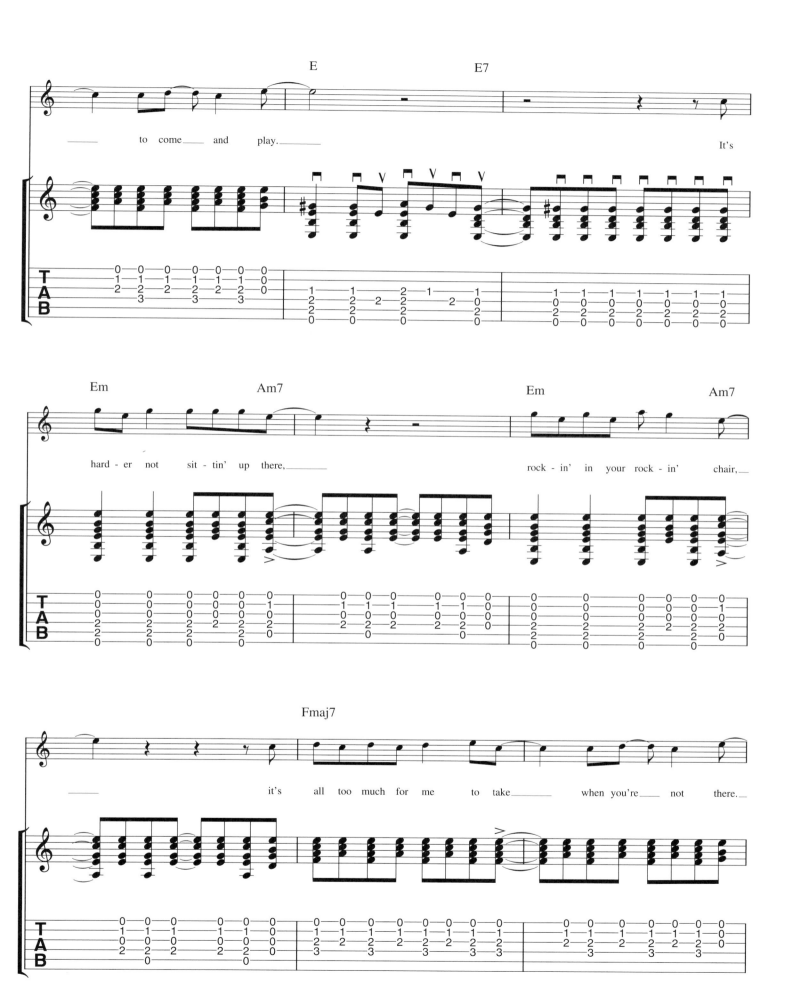

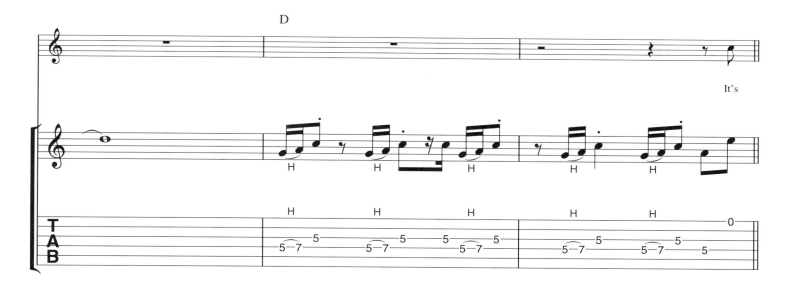

It's

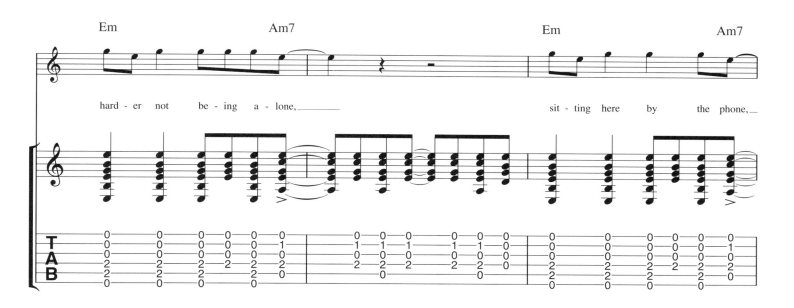

hard - er not   be - ing a - lone,_____   sit - ting here   by   the   phone,_

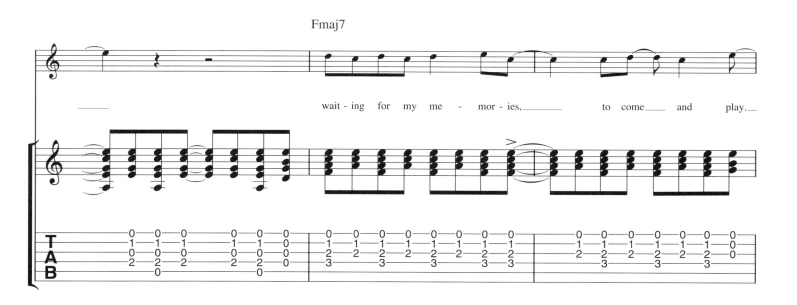

_____   wait - ing for my me - mor - ies,_____   to come___ and   play._

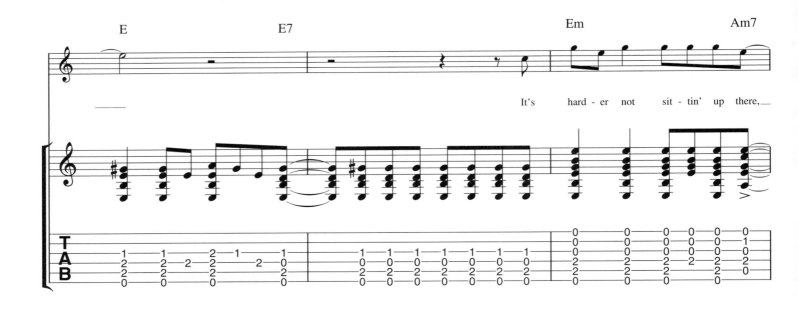

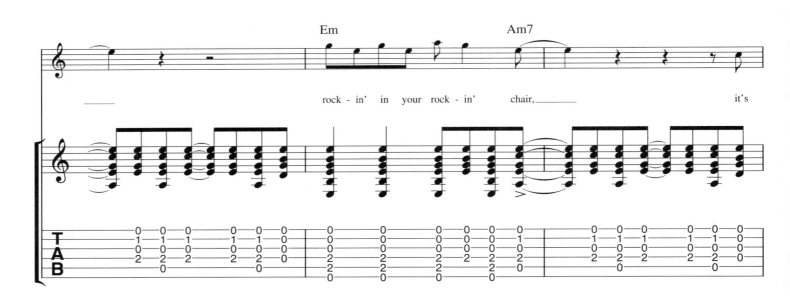

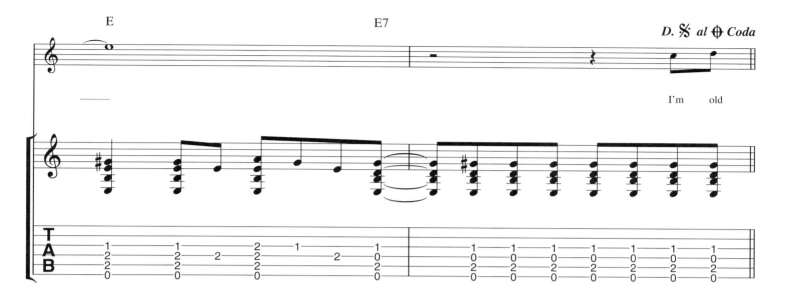

I'm   old

Hold . .

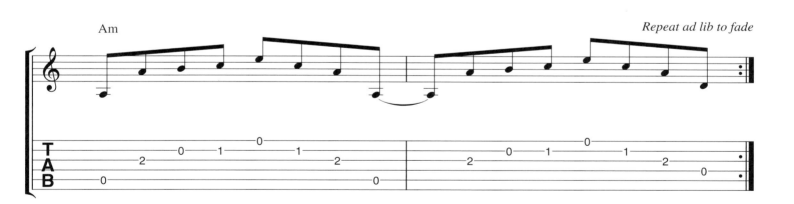

Repeat ad lib to fade

Round Are Way

Words & Music by Noel Gallagher

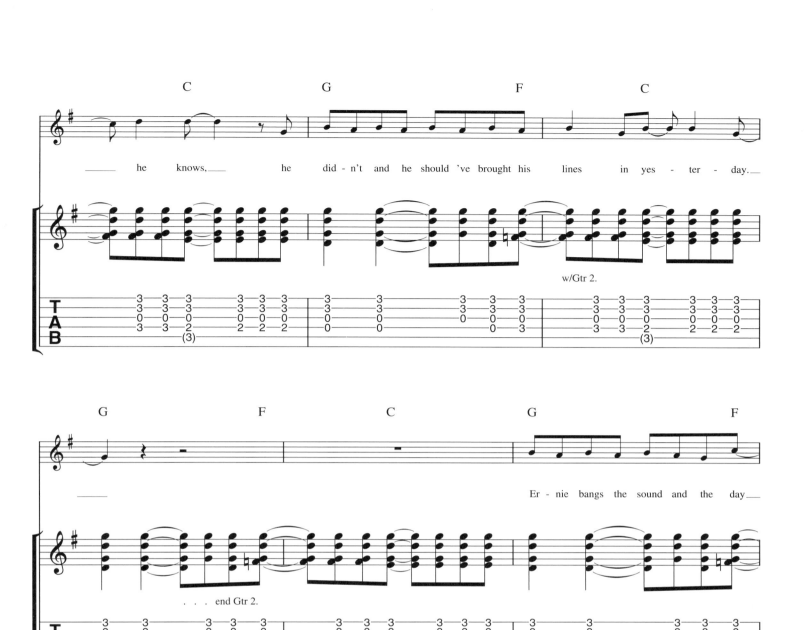

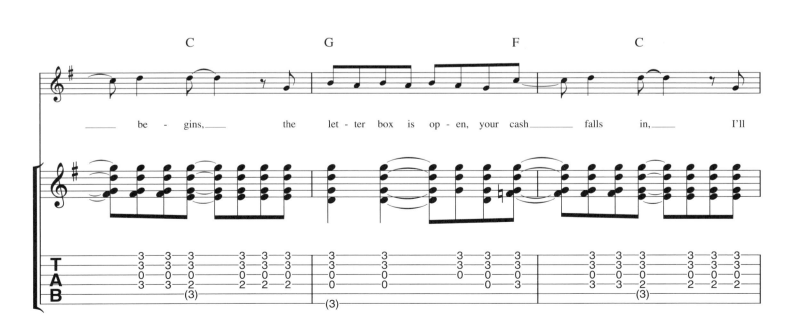

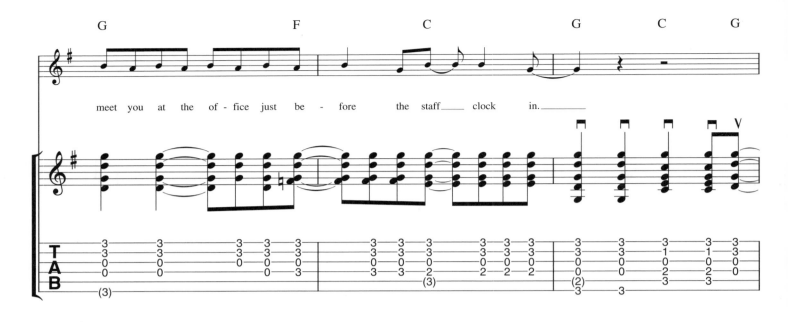

meet you at the of - fice just be - fore the staff___ clock in.___

Chorus:

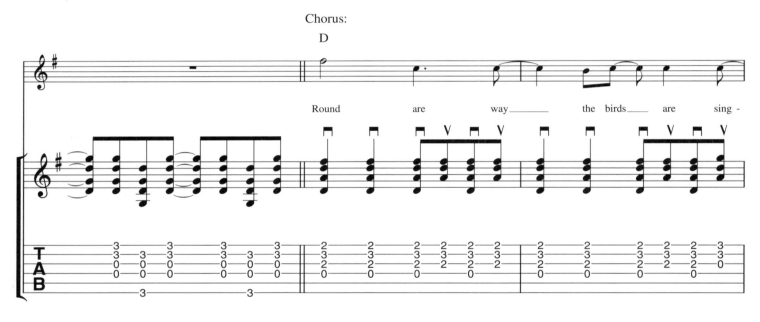

Round are way___ the birds___ are sing -

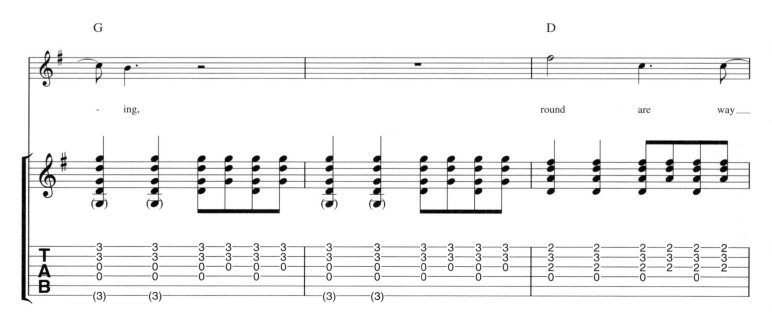

- ing, round are way___

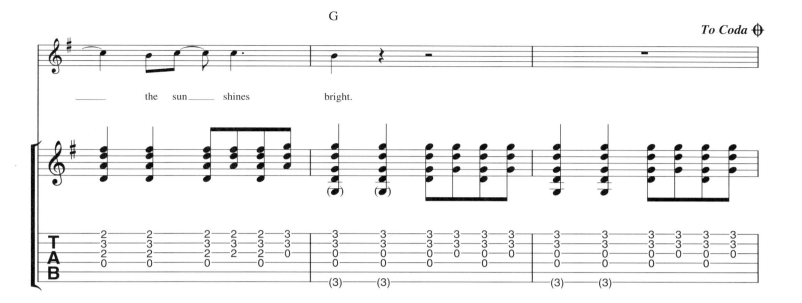

the sun___ shines bright.

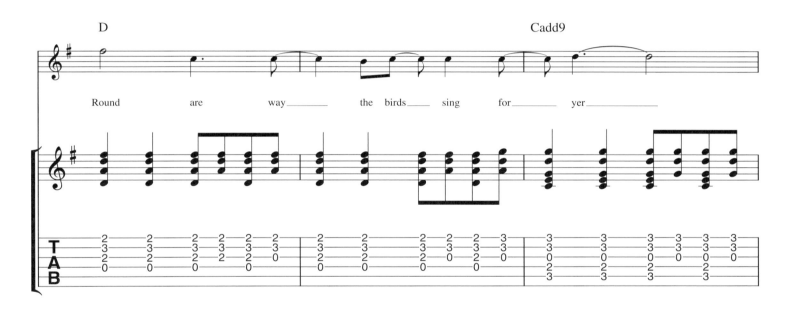

Round___ are___ way___ the birds___ sing for___ yer___

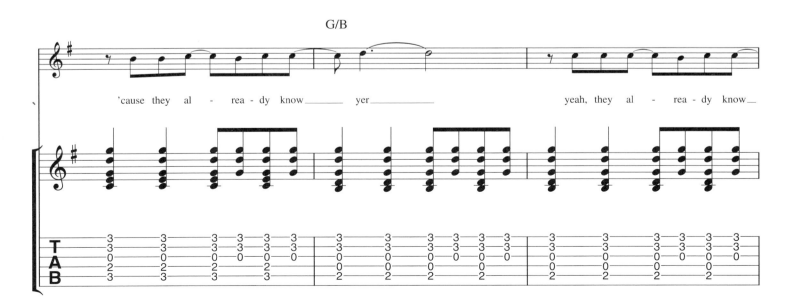

'cause they al - rea - dy know___ yer___ yeah, they al - rea - dy know___

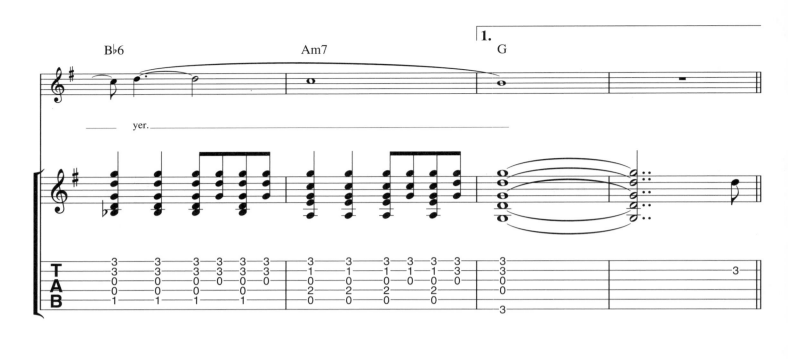

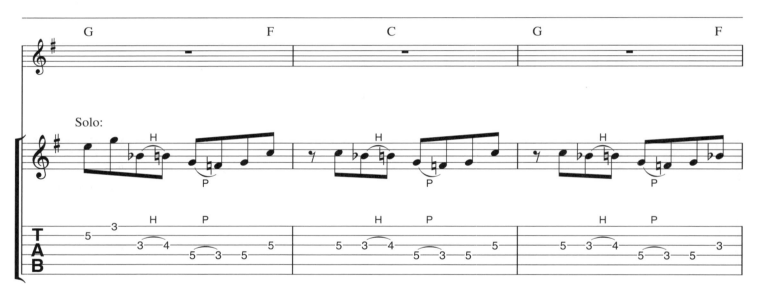

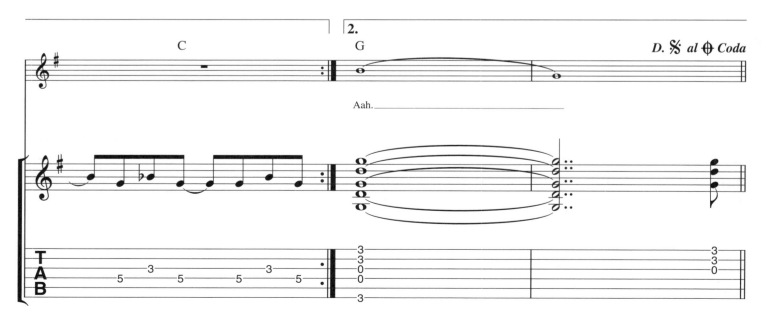

Coda ⊕   D   G

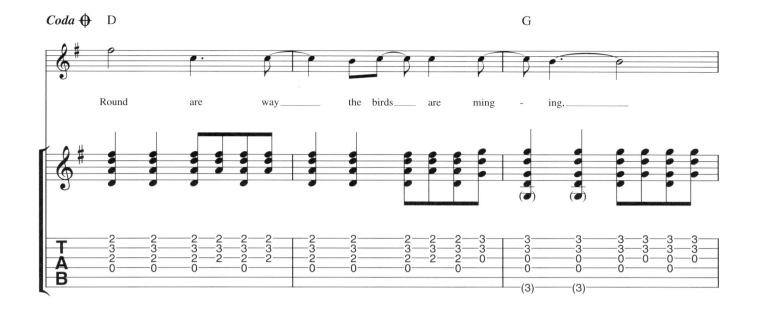

Round   are   way_____   the birds_____   are   ming - ing,_____

                                        D

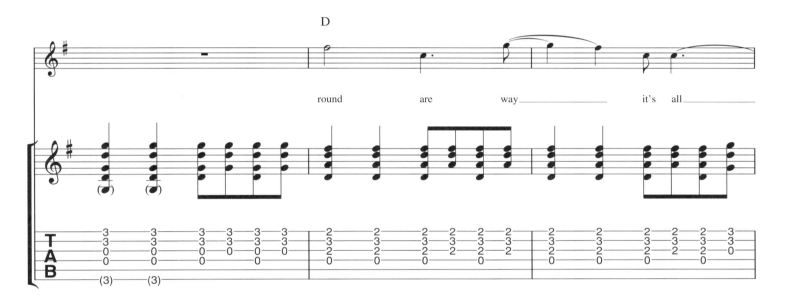

round   are   way_____   it's   all_____

G   D

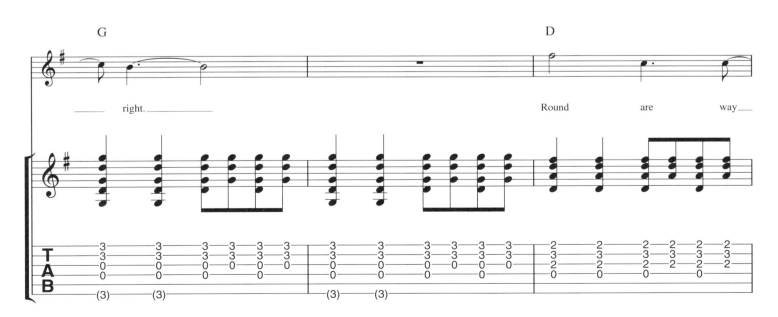

_____   right._____   Round   are   way_____

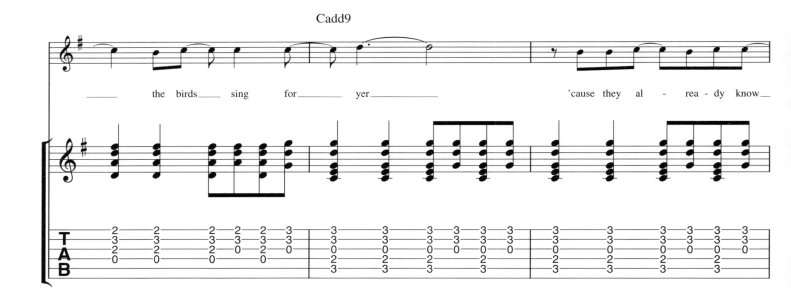

the birds___ sing for___ yer___ 'cause they al - rea - dy know___

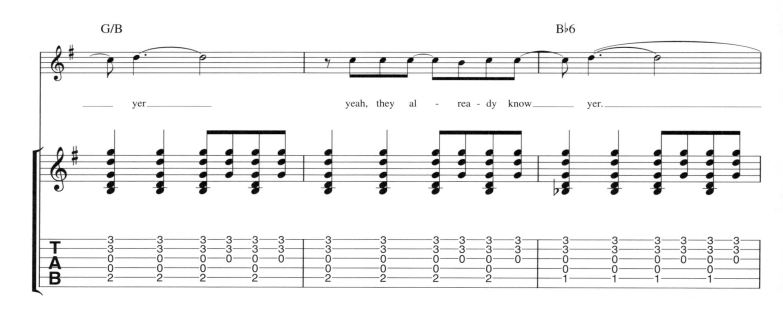

___ yer___ yeah, they al - rea - dy know___ yer.___

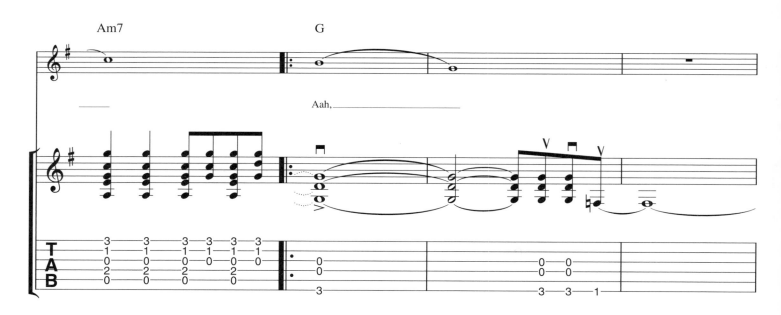

Aah,___

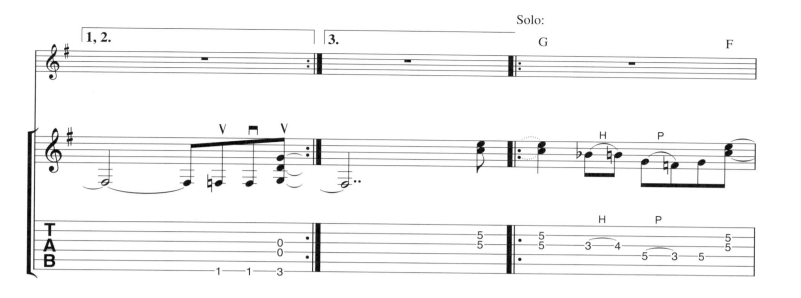

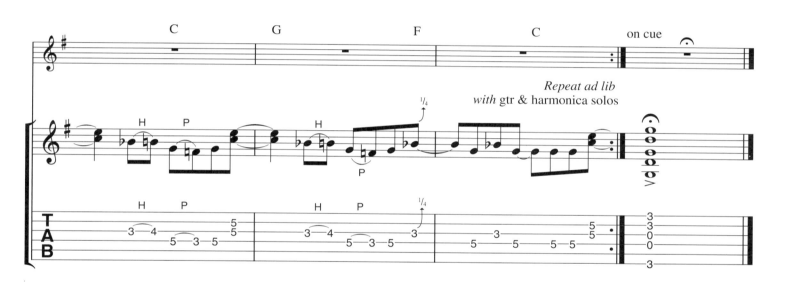

Verse 2:   The game is kicking off in around the park
It's twenty five a side and before it's dark
There's gonna be a loser
And you know the next goal wins
Cab it to the front as it's called a draw
Everybody's knockin' at yours once more
Ernie bangs the sound
And no one's spoken since half past four.

Step Out

Words & Music by Noel Gallagher, Henry Cosby, Stevie Wonder & Sylvia Moy

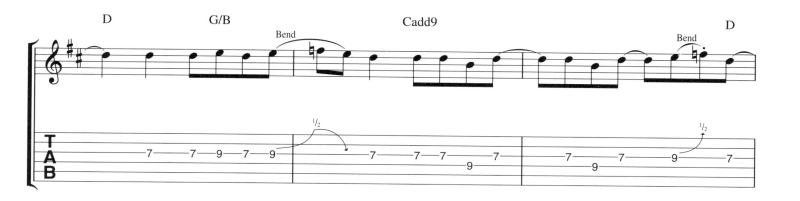

Verse:

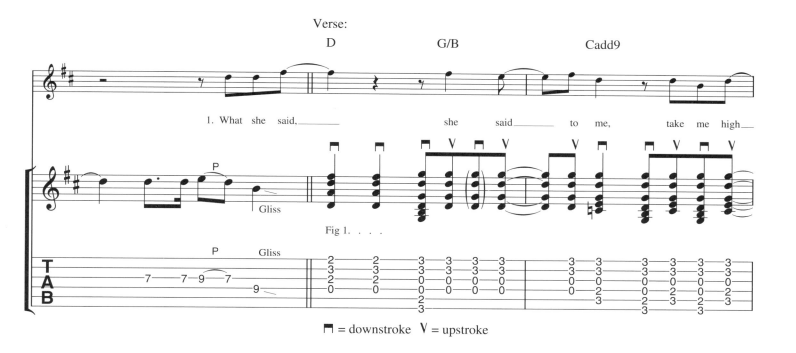

1. What she said,_____ she said_____ to me, take me high_____

Fig 1. . . .

⊓ = downstroke V = upstroke

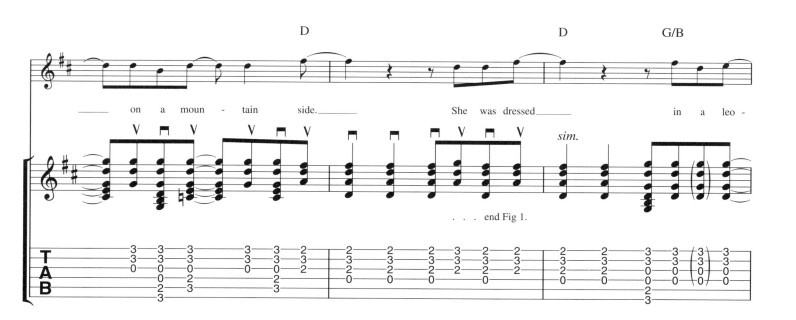

_____ on a moun - tain side._____ She was dressed_____ in a leo -

. . . end Fig 1.

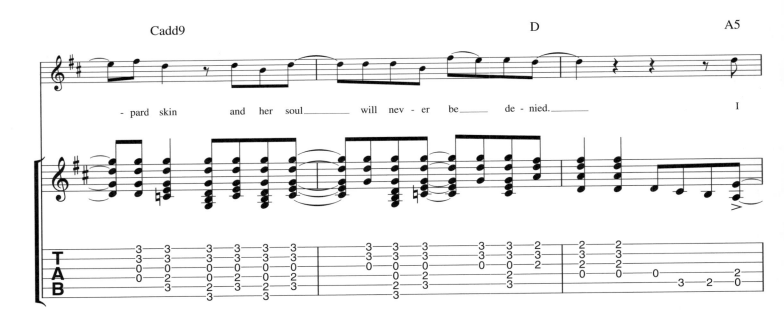

- pard skin and her soul_____ will nev - er be_____ de - nied._____

met her down the dis - co in a beat up car,____ she was burn - ing down the road.

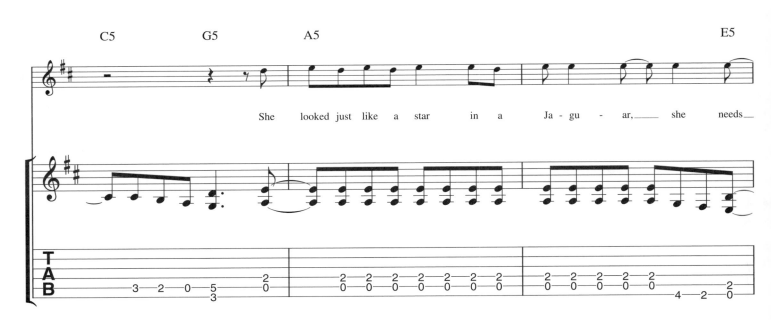

She looked just like a star in a Ja - gu - ar,____ she needs_____

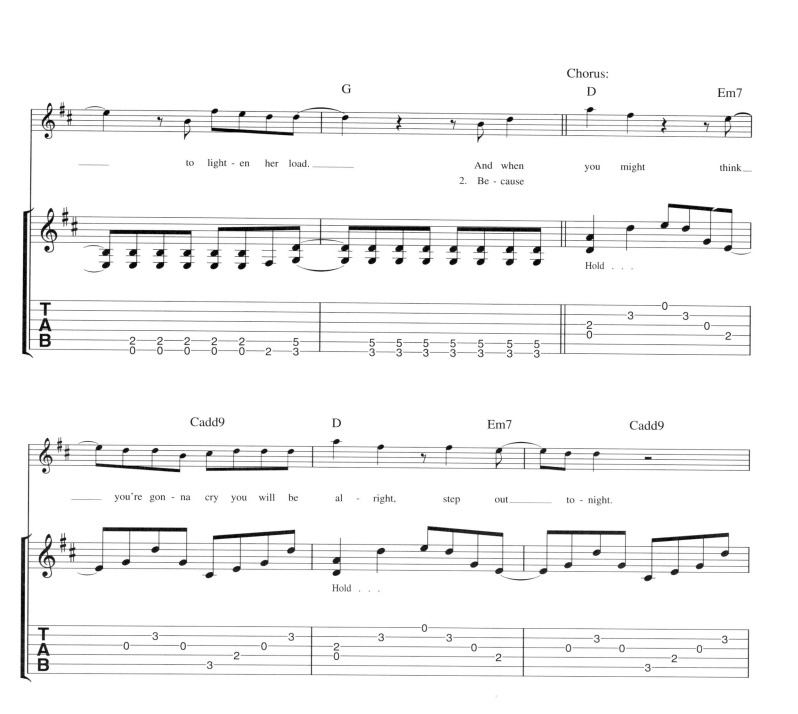

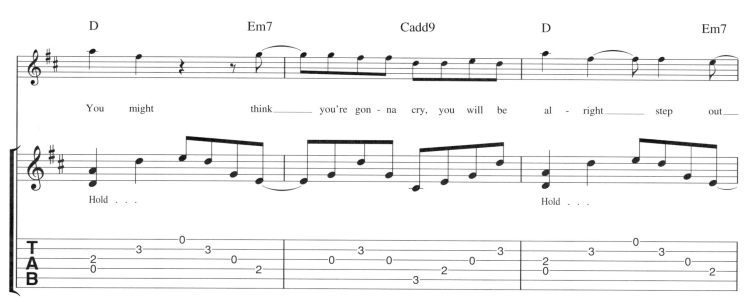

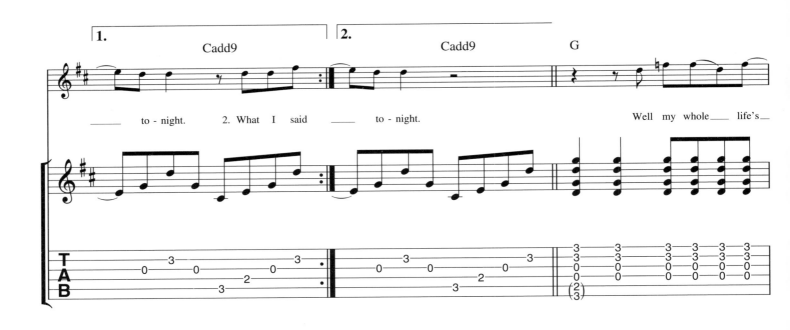

to - night.   2. What I said   to - night.   Well my whole___ life's

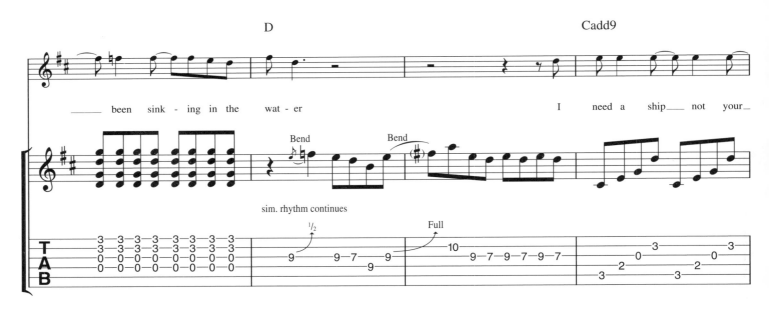

been sink - ing in the wat - er   I need a ship___ not your___

sim. rhythm continues

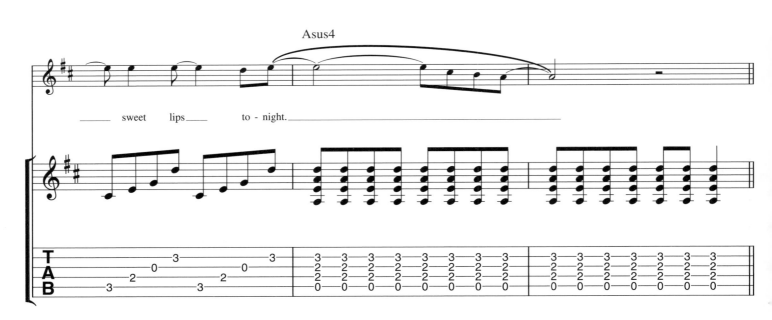

sweet lips___ to - night.

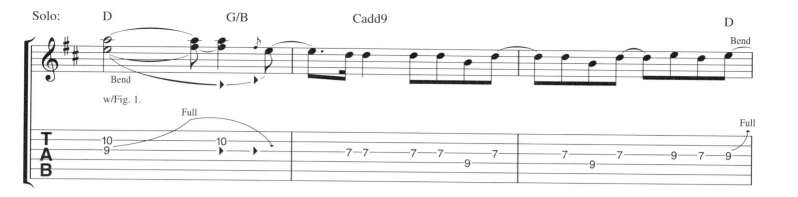

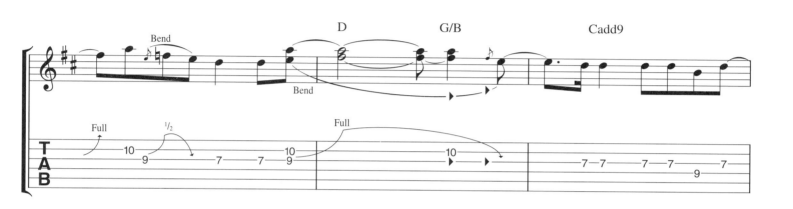

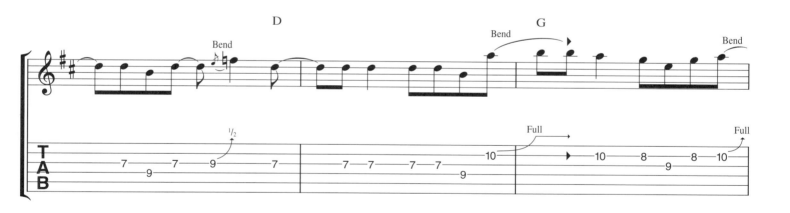

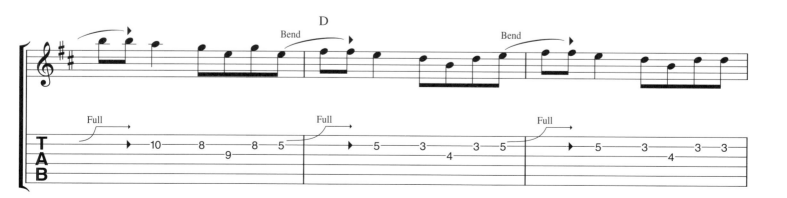

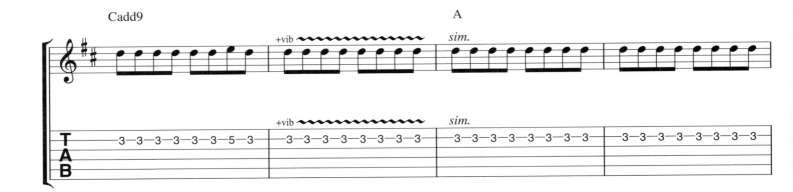

Chorus:

you might think you're gon - na cry you will be al - right, step out___
Hold . . .   Hold . . .

___ to - night. You might think___ you're gon - na cry, you will be
Hold . . .

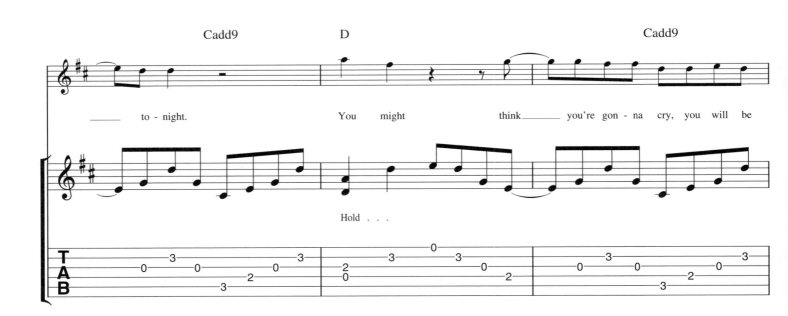

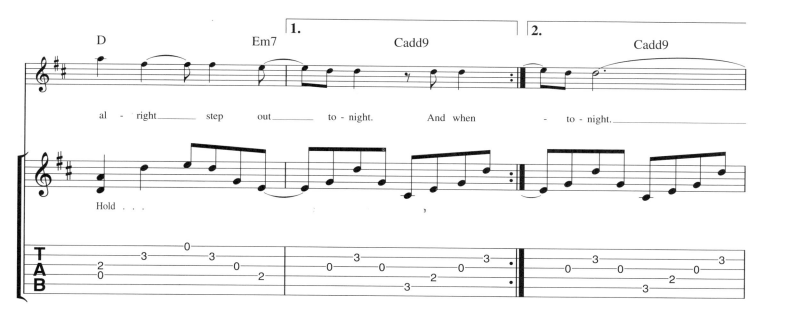

al - right_____ step out_____ to - night. And when _____ - to - night._____

Hold . . .

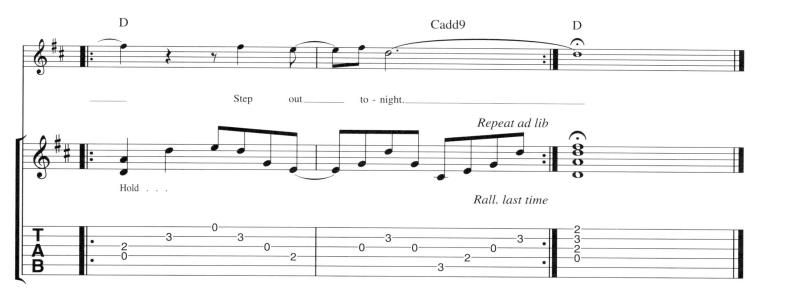

_____ Step out_____ to - night._____

Hold . . .

Repeat ad lib

Rall. last time

Verse 2:   What I said I said to her
             I'm alive when you walk that way
             Can you hear what I can hear
             It's the sound of a brand new day.

             She met me down a disco in a beat up car
             I was burning down the road
             I could be a star in a Jaguar
             I need to lighten my load.

Talk Tonight

Words & Music by Noel Gallagher

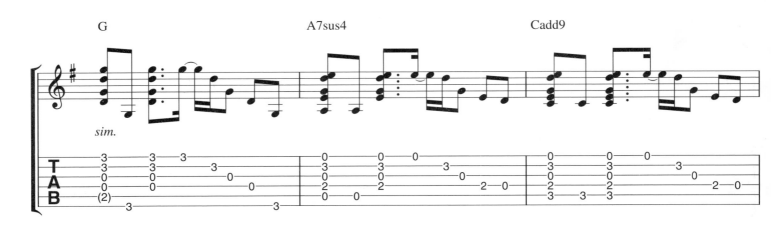

Verse:

Sit - ting on my own,   chew - ing on a bone a thou - sand mil - lion miles

See Block Lyrics for Verse 2

Hold . . . . .

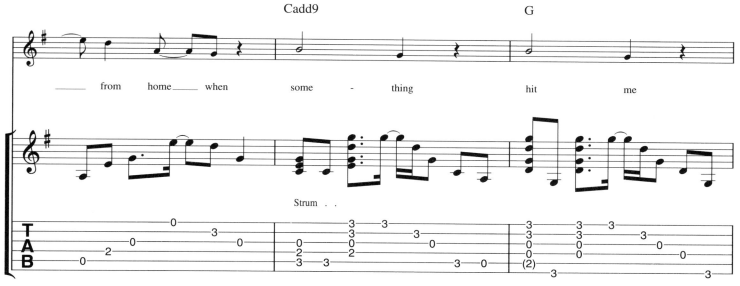

___ from home___ when   some - thing   hit   me

Strum . .

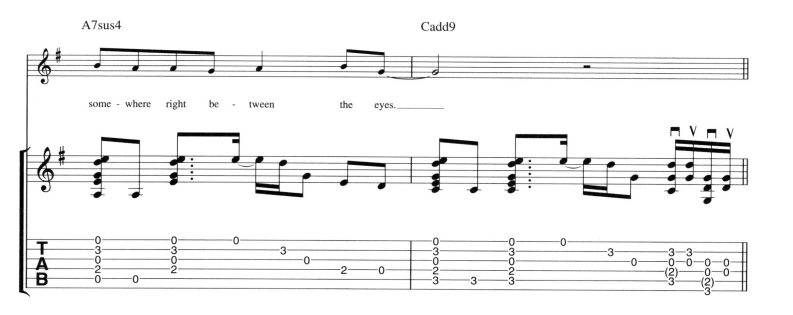

some - where right be - tween   the   eyes.___

Em   A7sus4

Sleep - ing on a plane, you know_____ you can't com - plain, you took_____ your last____ chance, once

Hold . . . . .

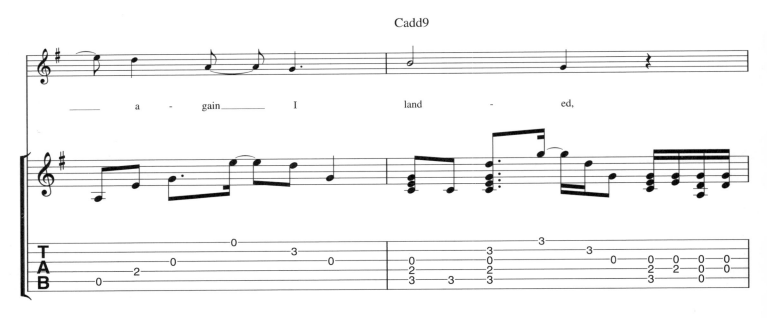

                                                Cadd9

_____ a - gain_____ I   land   -   ed,

G   A7sus4   Cadd9

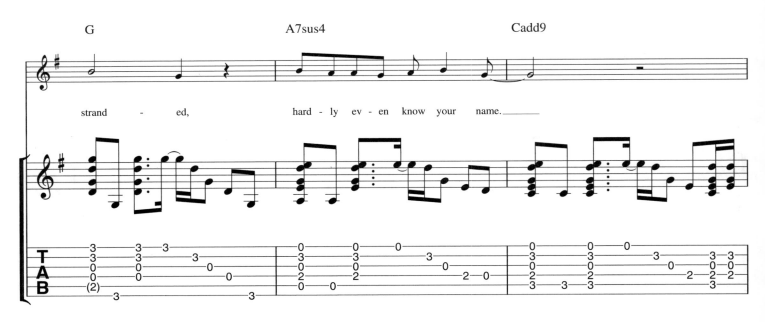

strand   -   ed,   hard - ly ev - en know your   name._____

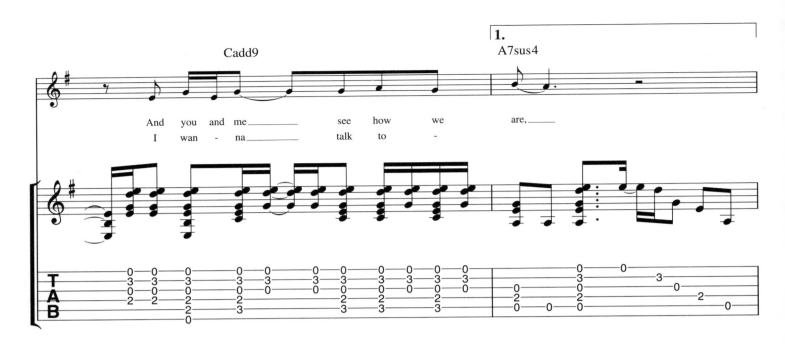

And you and me_____ see how we are,_____
I wan - na_____ talk to -

you and me_____ see how we are._____

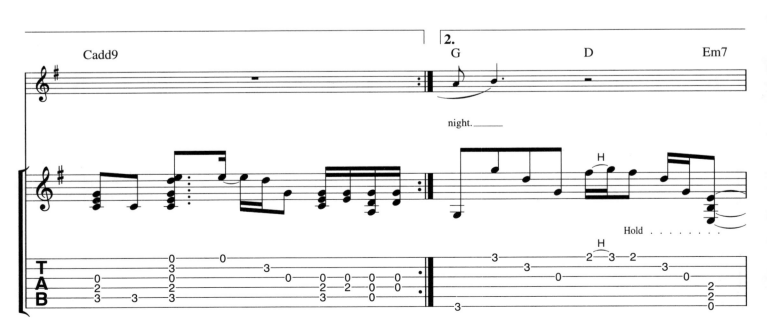

night._____

Hold . . . .

126

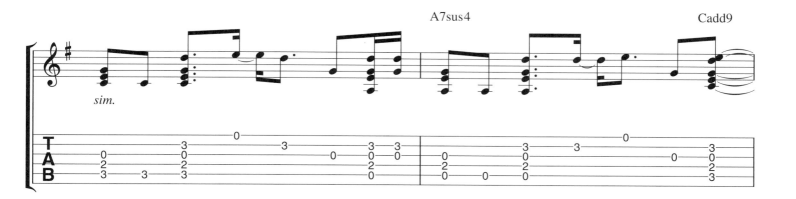

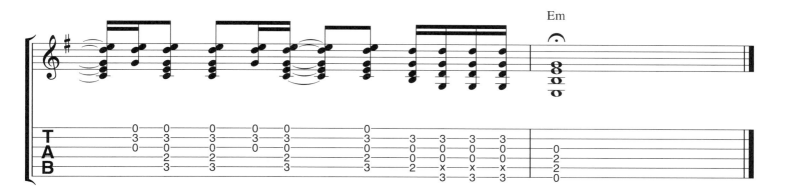

Verse 2:   All your dreams are made of strawberry lemonade
And you make sure I eat today
Take me walking
To where you played when you were young.

I'll never say that I won't ever make you cry
And this I'll say I don't know why
I know I'm leaving
But I'll be back another day.

The Masterplan

Words & Music by Noel Gallagher

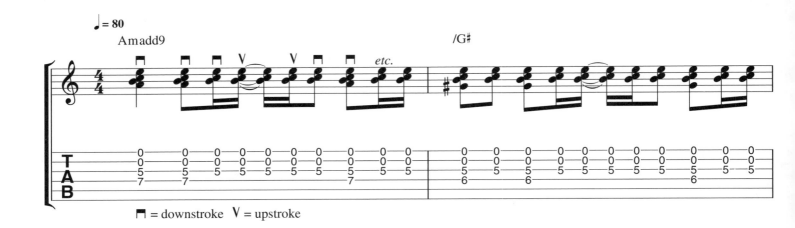

∏ = downstroke   V = upstroke

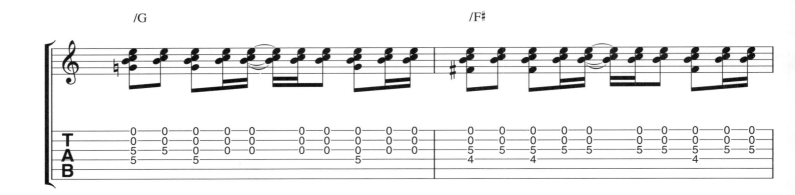

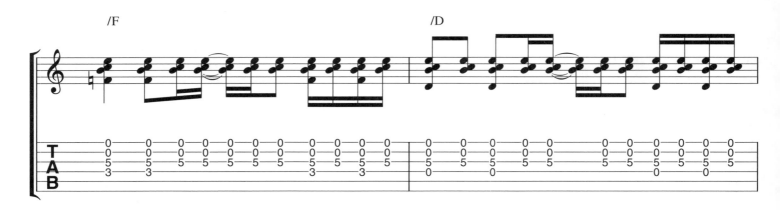

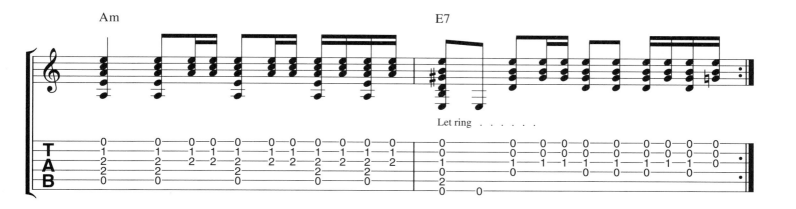

Verse:

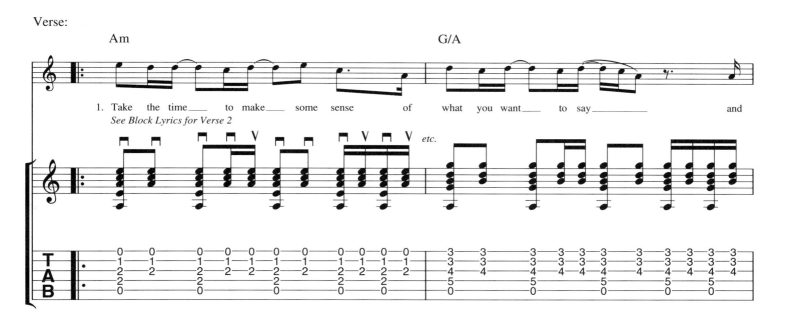

1. Take the time___ to make___ some sense of what you want___ to say___ and
See Block Lyrics for Verse 2

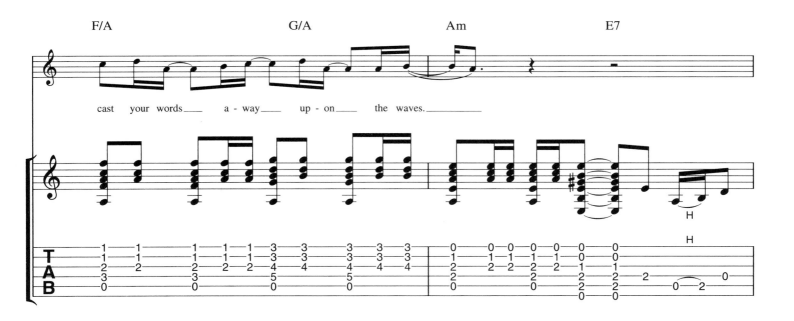

cast your words___ a - way___ up - on___ the waves.___

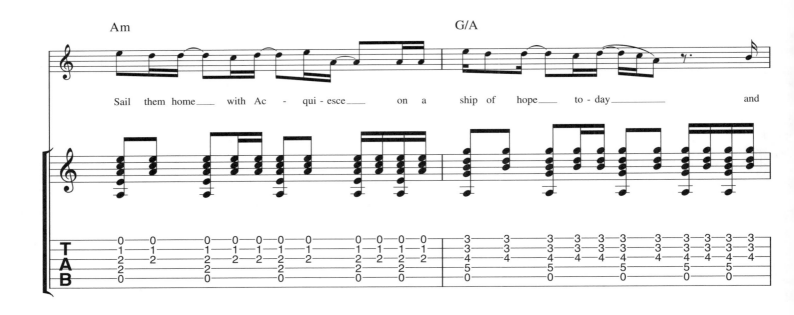

Am

G/A

Sail them home___ with Ac - qui -esce___ on a ship of hope to - day___ and

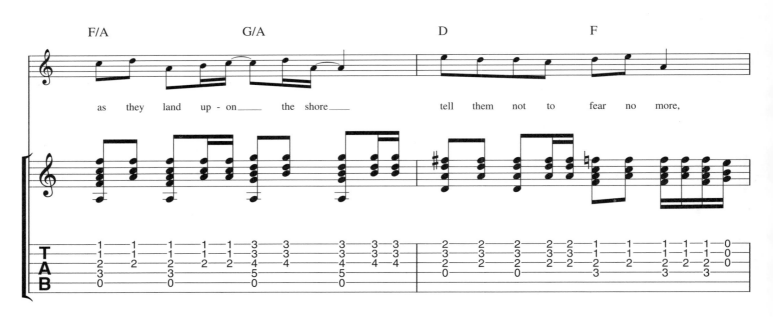

F/A

G/A

D

F

as they land up - on___ the shore___ tell them not to fear no more,

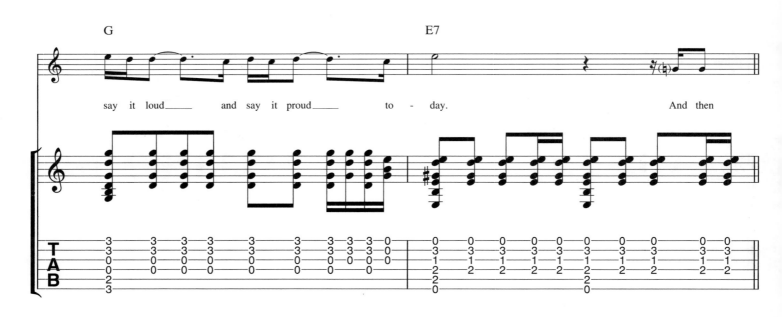

G

E7

say it loud___ and say it proud___ to - day. And then

dance if you wan-na dance, please broth-er take a chance, you know they're gon-na go which way they wan-na go.

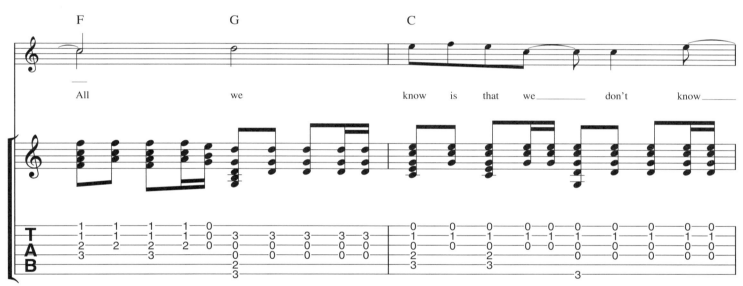

All we know is that we___ don't know___

___ how it's gon-na be, please broth-er let it be. Life on the oth-er hand won't make us un-der-stand,

we're all part of the mas- ter plan.

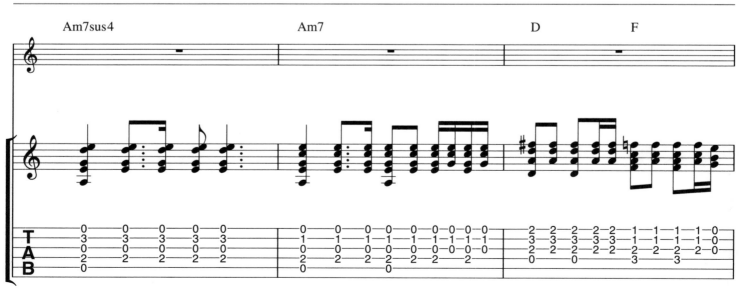

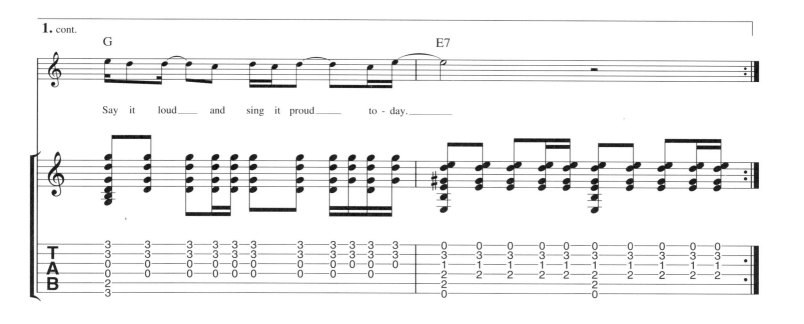

Say it loud___ and sing it proud___ to - day.___

Solo:

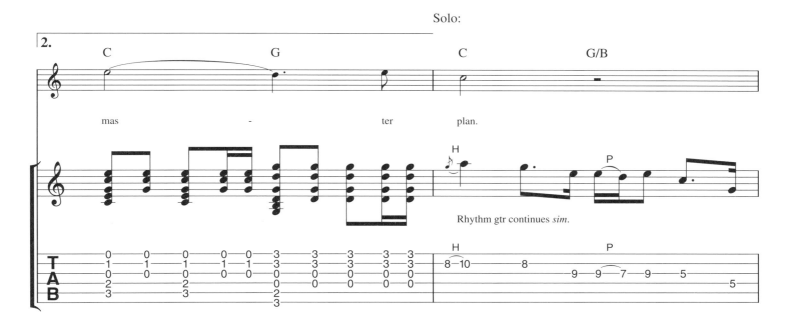

mas - ter plan.

Rhythm gtr continues *sim.*

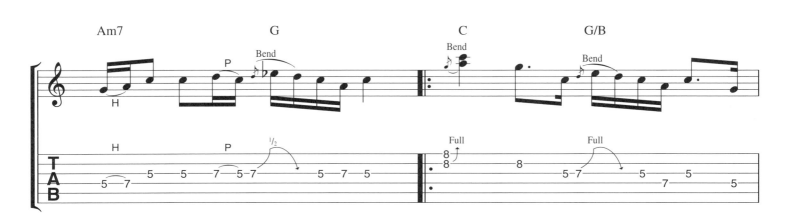

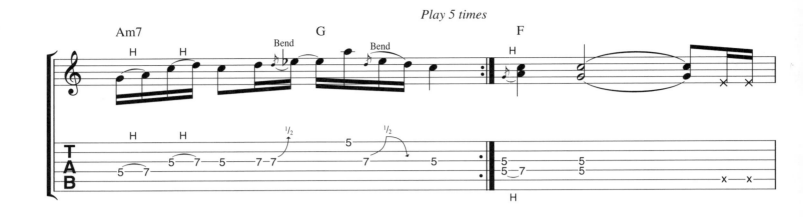

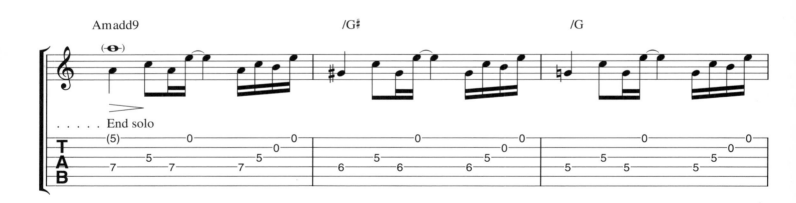

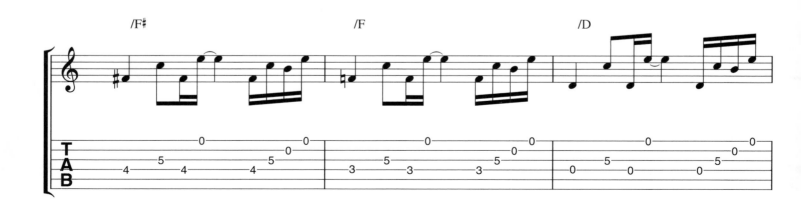

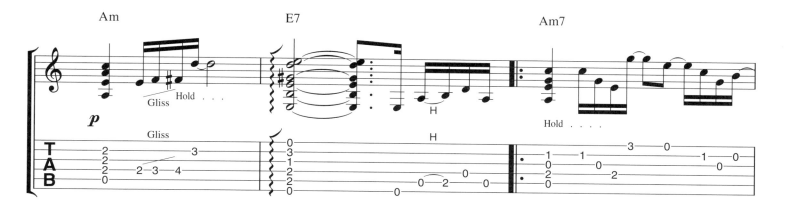

Play 3 times

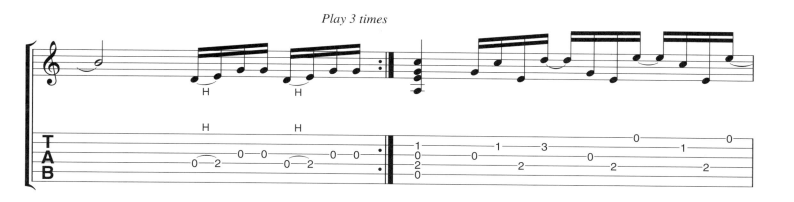

Verse 2:

I'm not saying right is wrong
It's up to us to make
The best of all the things that come our way
'Cos everything that's been has past
The answer's in the looking glass
There's four and twenty million doors
On life's endless corridor
Say it loud and sing it proud today.

Will dance if they want to dance
Please brother take a chance . . . *etc.*

Underneath The Sky

Words & Music by Noel Gallagher

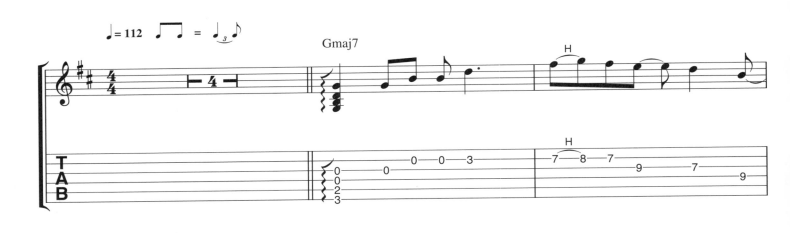

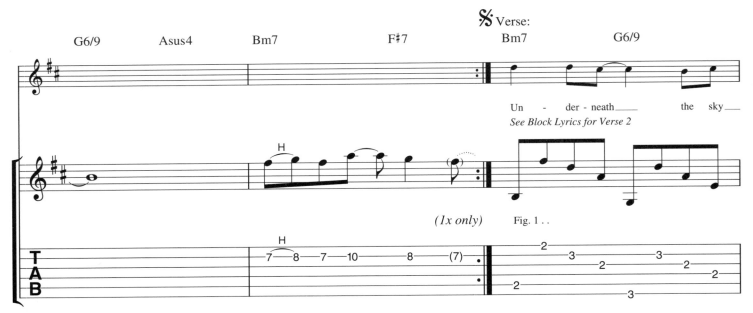

Un - der - neath___ the sky___
See Block Lyrics for Verse 2

139

to a friend___ of a friend_____ and as we drink___ to our-selves___ we'll am-use

sim.

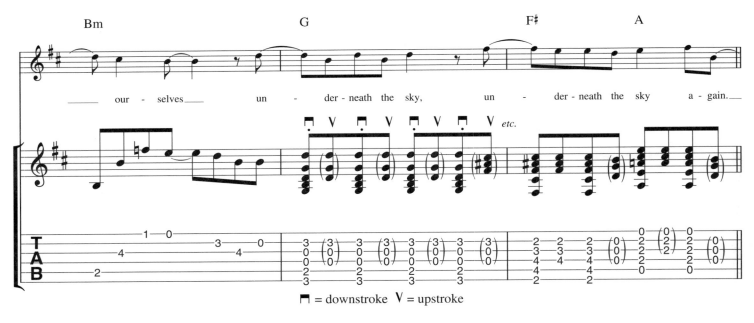

our-selves___ un - der-neath the sky, un - der-neath the sky a - gain.___

etc.

⊓ = downstroke   V = upstroke

Chorus:

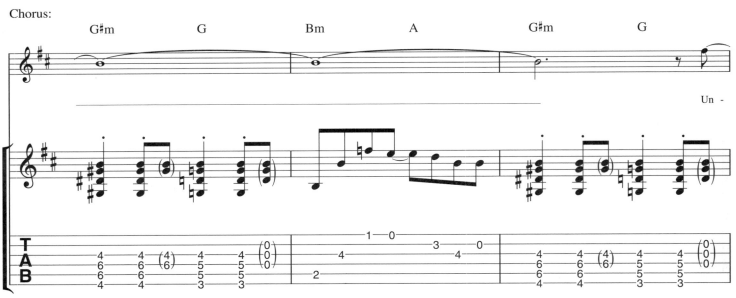

Un -

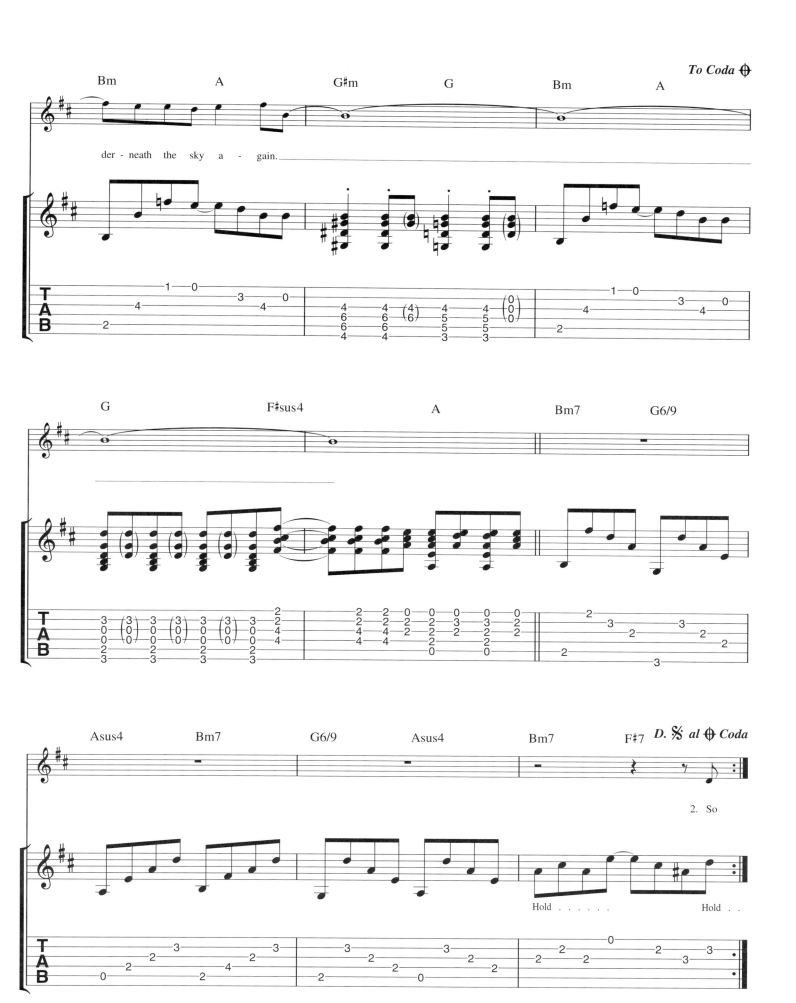

Coda ⊕

Un - der - neath the sky a - gain.

Un - der - neath the sky a - gain.

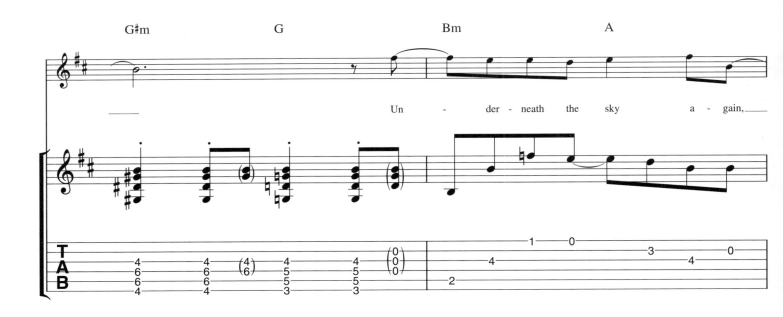

Un - der - neath the sky a - gain,

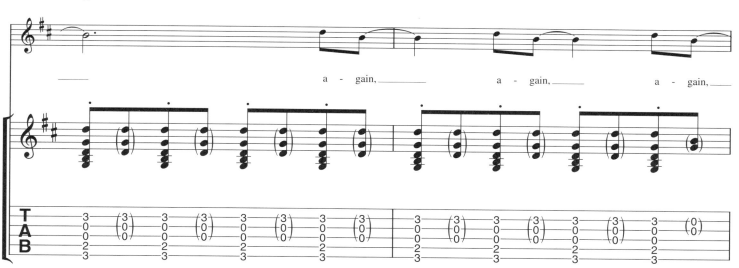

a - gain,_____ a - gain,_____ a - gain,_____

F#sus4   A   Bm

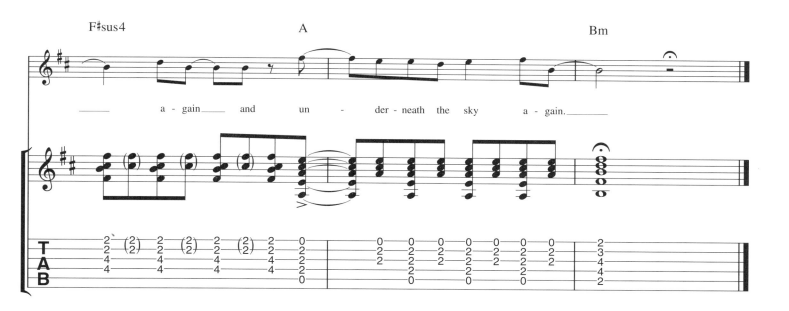

_____ a - gain_____ and un - der-neath the sky a - gain._____

Verse 2:   So wish me away to an unknown place
I'm living in a land with no name
I'll be making a start with my brand new heart
Stop me making sense once again.

All we need is our lives in a suitcase
They belong to a friend of a friend
And as we drink to ourselves we'll amuse ourselves
Underneath the sky, underneath the sky again.

Verse 3(%)   *Piano solo 8 bars*
All we need is our lives in a suitcase
They belong to a friend of a friend
And as we drink to ourselves we'll amuse ourselves
Underneath the sky, underneath the sky again.

The other side of OASIS

Exclusive Distributors:

Music Sales Limited
8/9 Frith Street,
London W1V 5TZ, England.

Music Sales Pty Limited
120 Rothschild Avenue,
Rosebery, NSW 2018, Australia.

Order No. AM939037
ISBN 0-7119-5951-X

Visit the Internet Music Shop at
http://www.musicsales.co.uk

Music arranged by Arthur Dick.
Music processed by Seton Music Graphics.
Book design by Michael Bell Design.
Front cover photograph courtesy of Jill Furmanovsky.

Printed in the United Kingdom by
Redwood Books Limited, Trowbridge, Wiltshire.

Your Guarantee of Quality:

As publishers, we strive to produce every
book to the highest commercial standards.

The music has been freshly engraved and the book
has been carefully designed to minimise awkward
page turns and to make playing from it a real pleasure.

Particular care has been given to specifying acid-free,
neutral-sized paper made from pulps which have
not been elemental chlorine bleached.

This pulp is from farmed sustainable forests and was
produced with special regard for the environment.

Throughout, the printing and binding have been
planned to ensure a sturdy, attractive publication
which should give years of enjoyment.

If your copy fails to meet our high standards,
please inform us and we will gladly replace it.

Music Sales' complete catalogue describes
thousands of titles and is available in full colour
sections by subject, direct from Music Sales Limited.
Please state your areas of interest and send a
cheque/postal order for £1.50 for postage to:
Music Sales Limited,
Newmarket Road, Bury St. Edmunds, Suffolk IP33 3YB.